WOLTT FIR
363.3790

Contents

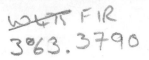
How to use this guide	2
Preface	3
Introduction	4
Part 1 Fire risk assessment	9
Step 1 Identify fire hazards	12
Step 2 Identify people at risk	14
Step 3 Evaluate, remove, reduce and protect from risk	15
Step 4 Record, plan, inform, instruct and train	35
Step 5 Review	42
Part 2 Further guidance on fire risk assessment and fire precautions	45
Section 1 Further guidance on fire risks and preventative measures	46
Section 2 Further guidance on fire-detection and warning systems	59
Section 3 Further guidance on firefighting equipment and facilities	63
Section 4 Further guidance on escape routes and strategies	70
Section 5 Further guidance on emergency escape lighting	111
Section 6 Further guidance on signs and notices	113
Section 7 Further guidance on recording, planning, informing, instructing and training	116
Section 8 Quality assurance of fire protection equipment and installation	127
Appendix A Example fire safety maintenance checklist	128
Appendix B Technical information on fire-resisting separation, fire doors and door fastenings	132
Appendix C Historic buildings	140
Appendix D Glossary	142
Appendix E Nucleus fire precautions	148
References	149
Further reading	153
Index	155

How to use this guide

This guide is divided into two parts:

- **Part 1** Explains what fire risk assessment is and how you might go about it. Fire risk assessment should be the foundation for all the fire precautions in your premises.

- **Part 2** Provides further guidance on fire precautions. The information is provided for you and others to dip into during your fire risk assessment or when you are reviewing your precautions.

The appendices provide example checklists, some detailed technical information on fire-resisting elements and advice on historic buildings.

This guide is one from a series of guides listed on the back cover.

The rest of this introduction explains how the law applies.

Technical terms are explained in the glossary and references to other publications listed at the end of the publication are identified by a superscript number in the text.

In this guide reference is made to British Standards, Department of Health Firecode and standards provided by other bodies. The standards referred to are intended for guidance only and other standards could be used. Reference to any particular standard is not intended to confer a presumption of conformity with the requirements of the Regulatory Reform (Fire Safety) Order 2005 (the Order).[1]

The level of necessary safety (or service) must be dictated by the findings of your risk assessment so you may need to do more or less than that specified in any particular standard referred to. You must be prepared to show that what you have done complies with any requirements or prohibitions of the Order[1] irrespective of whether you have relied on a particular standard.

Preface

This guidance gives advice on how to avoid fires and how to ensure people's safety if a fire does start. Why should you read it? Because:

- Fire kills. In 2004 England and Wales fire and rescue services attended over 33,400 fires in non-domestic buildings. These fires killed 38 people and injured over 1,300.

- Fire costs money. The costs of a serious fire can be high and afterwards many businesses do not reopen. In 2004, the costs as a consequence of fire, including property damage, human casualties and lost business were estimated at £2.5 billion.

This guide applies to England and Wales only. It does not set prescriptive standards, but provides recommendations and guidance for use when assessing the adequacy of fire precautions in premises providing healthcare. Other fire risk assessment methods may be equally valid to comply with fire safety law. The guide also provides recommendations for the fire safety management of the premises.

Your existing fire safety arrangements may not be the same as the recommendations used in this guide but, as long as you can demonstrate that they meet an equivalent standard of fire safety, they are likely to be acceptable. If you decide that your existing arrangements are not satisfactory there may be other ways to comply with fire safety law. This means there is no obligation to adopt any particular solution in this guide if you prefer to meet the relevant requirement in some other way.

Where the building has been recently constructed or significantly altered, the fire-detection and warning arrangements, escape routes and facilities for the fire and rescue service should have been designed, constructed and installed in line with current building regulations by following HTM 81[76] or its successor HTM 05–02: Part A.[76] In such cases, it is likely that these measures will be satisfactory as long as they are being properly maintained and no significant increase in risk has been introduced.

This guide should not be used to design fire safety in new buildings. Where alterations are proposed to existing premises, they may be subject to the building regulations or HTM 05-02: Part A.[76] However, it can be used to develop the fire safety strategy for the building.

Introduction

WHO SHOULD USE THIS GUIDE?

This guide is for all employers, managers, occupiers and owners of premises providing healthcare (including private healthcare premises). Details of other guides in the series are given on the back cover. It tells you what you have to do to comply with fire safety law, helps you to carry out a fire risk assessment and identify the general fire precautions you need to have in place.

It applies to premises where the main use of the building or part of the building is to provide healthcare and includes:

• hospitals; and

• other healthcare premises.

It may also be suitable for individual healthcare premises that are within other multi-use complexes, although consultation with other responsible people will be necessary as part of an integrated risk assessment for the complex.

Also, where you handle and store flammable material and substances, it will help you take account of these in your risk assessment and help you determine the necessary precautions to take to minimise the likelihood of them being involved in fire.

This guide is not intended for use in:

• care and nursing homes (other than those where the primary purpose is the provision of healthcare);

• rehabilitation premises providing residential treatment and care for various forms of addiction;

• day-care centres with no residential clients or service users;

• sheltered accommodation;

• out-posted nursing care in single private dwellings;

• staff accommodation; and

• administration blocks.

It has been written to provide guidance for a responsible person, to help them carry out a fire risk assessment in less complex premises. If you read the guide and decide that you are unable to apply the guidance, then you should seek the expert advice of a competent person. More complex premises will probably need to be assessed by a person who has comprehensive training or experience in fire risk assessment. However, this guide can be used to address fire safety issues within the individual occupancies of multi-occupied buildings.

It may also be useful for:

- employees;

- employee-elected representatives;

- trade union-appointed health and safety representatives;

- enforcing authorities; and

- all other people who have a role in ensuring fire safety in premises providing healthcare.

If your premises are listed as of historic interest, also see Appendix C.

Fire safety is only one of many safety issues with which management must concern themselves to minimise the risk of injury or death to staff, patients or visitors. Unlike most of the other safety concerns, fire has the potential to injure or kill large numbers of people very quickly. This guidance is concerned only with fire safety but many of the measures discussed here will impact upon other safety issues. It is recognised that these differing safety demands can sometimes affect one another and management should consult other interested agencies such as the Health and Safety Executive (HSE), where necessary, to confirm that they are not contravening other legislation/guidance.

You can get advice about minimising fire losses from your insurer or your competent fire adviser.

THE FIRE SAFETY ORDER

Previous general fire safety legislation

The Order[1] replaces previous fire safety legislation. Any fire certificate issued under the Fire Precautions Act 1971[2] will cease to have any effect. If a fire certificate has been issued in respect of any part of your premises or the premises were built in accordance with building regulations or HTM 81[76] or HTM 05-02: Part A,[76] as long as you have made no material alterations and all the physical fire precautions have been properly maintained, then it is unlikely you will need to make any significant improvements to your existing physical fire protection arrangements to comply with the Order.[1] However, you must still carry out a fire risk assessment and keep it up to date to ensure that all the fire precautions in your premises remain current and adequate.

If you have previously carried out a fire risk assessment under the Fire Precautions (Workplace) Regulations 1997,[3] as amended 1999,[4] and this assessment has been regularly reviewed, then all you will need to do now is revise that assessment taking account of the wider scope of the Order[1] as described in this guide.

Introduction and the responsibilities of the responsible person

The Order[1] applies in England and Wales. It covers 'general fire precautions' and other fire safety duties which are needed to protect 'relevant persons' in case of fire in and around most 'premises'. The Order[1] requires fire precautions to be put in place 'where necessary' and to the extent that it is reasonable and practicable in the circumstances of the case.

Responsibility for complying with the Order[1] rests with the 'responsible person'. In a workplace, this is the employer and any other person who may have control of any part of the premises, e.g. the occupier or owner. In all other premises the person or people in control of the premises will be responsible. If there is more than one responsible person in any type of premises (e.g. a multi-occupied complex), all must take all reasonable steps to co-operate and co-ordinate with each other.

If you are the responsible person you must carry out a fire risk assessment which must focus on the safety in case of fire of all 'relevant persons'. It should pay particular attention to those at special risk, such as disabled people, those who you know have special needs and children, and must include consideration of any dangerous substance liable to be on the premises. Your fire risk assessment will help you identify risks that can be removed or reduced and to decide the nature and extent of the general fire precautions you need to take.

If your organisation employs five or more people, your premises are licensed or an alterations notice is in force, you must record the significant findings of the assessment. It is good practice to record your significant findings in any case.

There are some other fire safety duties you need to comply with:

- **You must** appoint one or more 'competent persons', depending on the size and use of your premises, to carry out any of the preventive and protective measures required by the Order[1] (you can nominate yourself for this purpose). A competent person is someone with enough training and experience or knowledge and other qualities to be able to implement these measures properly.

- **You must** provide your employees with clear and relevant information on the risks to them identified by the fire risk assessment, about the measures you have taken to prevent fires, and how these measures will protect them if a fire breaks out.

- **You must** consult your employees (or their elected representatives) about nominating people to carry out particular roles in connection with fire safety and about proposals for improving the fire precautions.

- **You must**, before you employ a child, provide a parent with clear and relevant information on the risks to that child identified by the risk assessment, the measures you have put in place to prevent/protect them from fire and inform any other responsible person of any risks to that child arising from their undertaking.

- **You must** inform non-employees, such as temporary or contract workers, of the relevant risks to them, and provide them with information about who are the nominated competent persons, and about the fire safety procedures for the premises.

- **You must** co-operate and co-ordinate with other responsible persons who also have premises in the building, inform them of any significant risks you find and how you will seek to reduce/control those risks which might affect the safety of their employees.

- **You must** provide the employer of any person from an outside organisation who is working in your premises (e.g. an agency providing temporary staff) with clear and relevant information on the risks to those employees and the preventive and protective measures taken. You must also provide those employees with appropriate instructions and relevant information about the risks to them.

- If you are not the employer but have any control of premises which contain more than one workplace, **you are also responsible** for ensuring that the requirements of the Order[1] are complied with in those parts over which you have control.

- **You must** consider the presence of any dangerous substances and the risk this presents to relevant persons from fire.

- **You must** establish a suitable means of contacting the emergency services and provide them with any relevant information about dangerous substances.

- **You must** provide appropriate information, instruction and training to your employees, during their normal working hours, about the fire precautions in your workplace, when they start working for you, and from time to time throughout the period they work for you.

- **You must** ensure that the premises and any equipment provided in connection with firefighting, fire detection and warning, or emergency routes and exits are covered by a suitable system of maintenance and are maintained by a competent person in an efficient state, in efficient working order and in good repair.

- **Your employees must** co-operate with you to ensure the workplace is safe from fire and its effects, and must not do anything that will place themselves or other people at risk.

The above examples outline some of the main requirements of the Order.[1] The rest of this guide will explain how you might meet these requirements.

Who enforces the Fire Safety Order?

The local fire and rescue authority (the fire and rescue service) will enforce the Order[1] in most premises. The exceptions are:

- Crown-occupied/owned premises where Crown fire inspectors will enforce;

- premises within armed forces establishments, where the defence fire and rescue service will enforce; and

- certain specialist premises including construction sites, ships (under repair or construction) and nuclear installations, where the HSE will enforce; and

- sports grounds and stands designated as needing a safety certificate by the local authority, where the local authority will enforce.

The enforcing authority will have the power to inspect your premises to check that you are complying with your duties under the Order.[1] They will look for evidence that you have carried out a suitable fire risk assessment and acted upon the significant findings of that assessment. If, as is likely, you are required to record the outcome of the assessment they will expect to see a copy.

If the enforcing authority is dissatisfied with the outcome of your fire risk assessment or the action you have taken, they may issue an enforcement notice that requires you to make certain improvements or, in extreme cases, a prohibition notice that restricts the use of all or part of your premises until improvements are made.

If your premises are considered by the enforcing authority to be or have the potential to be high risk, they may issue an alterations notice that requires you to inform them before you make any changes to your premises or the way they are used.

Failure to comply with any duty imposed by the Order[1] or any notice issued by the enforcing authority is an offence. You have a right of appeal to a magistrates court against any notice issued. Where you agree that there is a need for improvements to your fire precautions but disagree with the enforcing authority on the technical solution to be used (e.g. what type of fire alarm system is needed) you may agree to refer this for an independent determination.

If having read this guide you are in any doubt about how fire safety law applies to you, contact the fire safety office at your local fire and rescue service.

If your premises were in use before 2006, then they may have been subject to the Fire Precautions Act[2] and the Fire Precautions (Workplace) Regulations.[3,4] Where the layout (means of escape) and other fire precautions have been assessed by the fire and rescue service to satisfy the guidance that was then current, it is likley that your premises already conform to many of the recommendations here, providing you have undertaken a fire risk assessment as required by the Fire Precautions (Workplace) Regulations.[3,4]

New buildings or significant building alterations should be designed to satisfy current building regulations[24] (which address fire precautions).

However, you will still need to carry out a fire risk assessment, or review your existing assessment, e.g. HTM 86[80] (and act on your findings), to comply with the Order.[1]

Part 1 Fire risk assessment

MANAGING FIRE SAFETY

Good management of fire safety is essential to ensure that fires are unlikely to occur; that if they do occur they are likely to be controlled or contained quickly, effectively and safely; or that, if a fire does occur and grow, everyone in your premises is able to escape to a place of total safety easily and quickly.

The risk assessment that you must carry out will help you ensure that your fire safety procedures, fire prevention measures, and fire precautions (plans, systems and equipment) are all in place and working properly, and the risk assessment should identify any issues that need attention. Further information on managing fire safety is available in Part 2 on page 45.

WHAT IS A FIRE RISK ASSESSMENT?

A fire risk assessment is an organised and methodical look at your premises, the activities carried on there and the likelihood that a fire could start and cause harm to those in and around the premises.

The aims of the fire risk assessment are:

• To identify the fire hazards.

• To reduce the risk of those hazards causing harm to as low as reasonably practicable.

• To decide what physical fire precautions and management arrangements are necessary to ensure the safety of people in your premises if a fire does start.

The term 'where necessary' (see Glossary) is used in the Order,[1] therefore when deciding what fire precautions and management arrangements are necessary, you will need to take account of this definition.

The terms 'hazard' and 'risk' are used throughout this guide and it is important that you have a clear understanding of how these should be used.

• **Hazard:** anything that has the potential to cause harm.

• **Risk:** the chance of that harm occurring.

If your organisation employs five or more people, or your premises are licensed or an alterations notice requiring it is in force, then the significant findings of the fire risk assessment, the actions to be taken as a result of the assessment and details of anyone especially at risk must be recorded. You will probably find it helpful to keep a record of the significant findings of your fire risk assessment even if you are not required to do so.

HOW DO YOU CARRY OUT A FIRE RISK ASSESSMENT?

A fire risk assessment will help you determine the chances of a fire starting and the dangers from fire that your premises present for the people who use them and any person in the immediate vicinity. The assessment method suggested in this guide shares the same approach as that used in general health and safety legislation and can be carried out either as part of a more general risk assessment or as a separate exercise. As you move through the steps there are checklists to help you.

Before you start your fire risk assessment, take time to prepare, and read through the rest of Part 1 of this guide.

Much of the information for your fire risk assessment will come from the knowledge your employees, colleagues and representatives have of the premises, as well as information given to you by people who have responsibility for other parts of the building. A tour of your premises will probably be needed to confirm, amend or add detail to your initial views.

It is important that you carry out your fire risk assessment in a practical and systematic way and that you allocate enough time to do a proper job. It must take the whole of your premises into account, including outdoor locations and any rooms and areas that are rarely used. If your premises are small (e.g. a stand-alone GP surgery) you may be able to assess them as a whole. In larger premises, such as a diagnostic and treatment centre, you may find it helpful to divide them into compartments or sub-compartments managed as a single unit using natural boundaries, e.g. process areas (such as patient treatment, kitchens or laundries), offices, stores, as well as corridors, stairways and external routes.

If your premises are in a multi-use complex then the information on hazard and risk reduction will still be applicable to you. However, any alterations to the use or structure of your individual unit will need to take account of the overall fire safety arrangements in the building.

Your premises may be simple, with few people present or with a limited degree of business activity, but if it forms part of a building with different occupancies, then the measures provided by other occupiers may have a direct effect on the adequacy of the fire safety measures in your premises.

Under health and safety law (enforced by the HSE or the local authority) you are required to carry out a risk assessment in respect of any work processes in your workplace and to take or observe appropriate special, technical or organisational measures. If your health and safety risk assessment identifies that these processes are likely to involve the risk of fire or the spread of fire (for example in the kitchen or in a workshop) then you will need to take this into account during your fire risk assessment under the Order,[1] and prioritise actions based on the level of risk.

You need to appoint one or more competent persons to carry out any of the preventive and protective measures needed to comply with the Order.[1] This person could be you, or an appropriately trained full-time employee or, where appropriate, a third party.

Your fire risk assessment should demonstrate that, as far as is reasonable, you have considered the needs of all relevant persons, including disabled people.

Figure 1 shows the five steps you need to take to carry out a fire risk assessment.

FIRE SAFETY RISK ASSESSMENT

1 Identify fire hazards

Identify:
Sources of ignition
Sources of fuel
Sources of oxygen

2 Identify people at risk

Identify:
People in and around the premises
People especially at risk

3 Evaluate, remove, reduce and protect from risk

Evaluate the risk of a fire occurring
Evaluate the risk to people from fire
Remove or reduce fire hazards
Remove or reduce the risks to people
- Detection and warning
- Fire-fighting
- Escape routes
- Lighting
- Signs and notices
- Maintenance

4 Record, plan, inform, instruct and train

Record significant finding and action taken
Prepare an emergency plan
Inform and instruct relevant people; co-operate and co-ordinate with others
Provide training

5 Review

Keep assessment under review
Revise where necessary

Remember to keep to your fire risk assessment under review.

Figure 1: The five steps of a fire risk assessment

STEP 1 IDENTIFYING FIRE HAZARDS

For a fire to start, three things are needed:

• a source of ignition;

• fuel; and

• oxygen.

If any one of these is missing, a fire cannot start. Taking measures to avoid the three coming together will therefore reduce the chances of a fire occurring.

The remainder of this step will advise on how to identify potential ignition sources, the materials that might fuel a fire and the oxygen supplies that will help it burn.

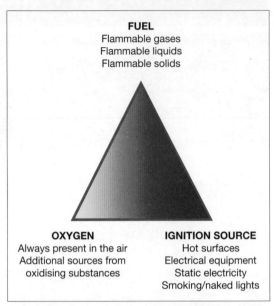

Figure 2: The fire triangle

1.1   Identify sources of ignition

You can identify the potential ignition sources in your premises by looking for possible sources of heat which could get hot enough to ignite material found in your premises. These sources could include:

• smoking materials, e.g. cigarettes, matches and lighters;

• naked flames, e.g. matches, candles or gas or liquid-fuelled open-flame equipment;

• electrical, gas or oil-fired heaters (fixed or portable);

• cooking equipment;

• faulty or misused electrical equipment;

• lighting equipment;

• hot surfaces and obstruction of equipment ventilation;

• hot processes, e.g. welding by contractors; and

• arson, e.g. by patients who suffer from mental illness.

Physiotherapy departments and X-ray departments can present a significant source of ignition.

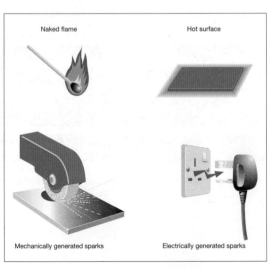

Figure 3: Sources of ignition

Fires may be started by patients, either accidentally or deliberately, particularly by those who:

• are elderly;

• have learning difficulties; or

• are young people with disabilities.

Those who suffer from mental illness may be particularly prone to starting fires.

Indications of 'near-misses', such as scorch marks on furniture or fittings, discoloured or charred electrical plugs and sockets, cigarette burns, etc, can help you identify hazards which you may not otherwise notice.

1.2   Identify sources of fuel

Anything that burns is fuel for a fire. You need to look for the things that will burn reasonably easily and are in enough quantity to provide fuel for a fire or cause it to spread to another fuel source. Some of the most common 'fuels' found in premises providing healthcare are:

• laundry supplies, such as bedding and towels, and medical supplies, such as disposable aprons;

• toiletries, aerosols, wall and ceiling hangings and linings;

• plastics and rubber (e.g. soft play or restraint areas), video tapes, polyurethane foam-filled furniture, foam-filled mats and polystyrene-based display materials;

• wood or wood-based furniture, textiles and soft furnishings, such as spare clothes and hanging curtains;

• clothing and private belongings (such as toys), seasonal and religious occasion decorations, such as Christmas decorations;

• flammable products, such as cleaning and decorating products, petrol, white spirit, methylated spirit, cooking oils, disposable cigarette lighters and photocopier chemicals;

• flammable gases such as liquefied petroleum gas (LPG), including aerosol canisters; and

• waste products, particularly finely divided items such as shredded paper and wood shavings, off cuts, and dust.

You should also consider the materials used to line walls and ceilings, e.g. polystyrene or carpet tiles, the fixtures and fittings and bought-in materials, and how they might contribute to the spread of fire. Further information is available in Part 2, Section 1.

1.3   Identify sources of oxygen

The main source of oxygen for a fire is in the air around us. In an enclosed building this is provided by the ventilation system in use. This generally falls into one of two categories: natural airflow through doors, windows and other openings; or mechanical air conditioning systems and air handling systems. In many buildings there will be a combination of systems, which will be capable of introducing/extracting air to and from the building.

Additional sources of oxygen can sometimes be found in materials used or stored at premises such as:

Figure 4: Label on oxidising materials

- some chemicals (oxidising materials), which can provide a fire with additional oxygen and so help it burn. These chemicals should be identified on their container (and Control of Substances Hazardous to Health (COSHH) data sheet, see Figure 4) by the manufacturer or supplier who can advise as to their safe use and storage; or

- oxygen supplies from cylinder storage and piped systems, e.g. medical oxygen, oxygen used by contractors (e.g. in welding processes).

Checklist

- Have you identified all potential ignition sources? ☐

- Have you identified all potential fuel sources? ☐

- Have you identified all potential sources of oxygen? ☐

- Have you made a note of your findings? ☐

STEP 2   IDENTIFYING PEOPLE AT RISK

As part of your fire risk assessment, you need to identify those at risk if there is a fire. To do this you need to identify where you have patients present and staff working (either at permanent workstations or at occasional locations around the premises) and to consider who else may be at risk, such as visitors, visiting contractors, etc, and where these people are likely to be found.

You must consider all the people who use the premises but you should pay particular attention to people who may be especially at risk such as:

- employees who work alone, either regularly or at specific times and/or in isolated areas, e.g. cleaners, security staff, maintenance staff, nursing or care staff (especially at night);

- people who are unfamiliar with the premises, e.g. agency or temporary staff, guests, visitors (including visiting medical or social care staff), contractors;

- patients who are unable to escape unaided (young children, babies, the elderly, physically disabled people (in particular people with mobility impairment), mentally disabled people, people with vision or hearing impairment, those with some other sensory impairment, and those whose ability to escape unassisted is impaired due to their medical condition or medication, or who who may be intoxicated);

- people who are not able to leave the premises quickly (but do not require assistance), e.g. patients or visitors who are elderly or with limited disabilities,* parents with children;

- people with language difficulties; or

- other persons in the immediate vicinity of the premises.

In evaluating the risk to people with disabilities you may need to discuss individual needs with each relevant person. The risk assessment should take into account the patient's medical conditions, sensory awareness and mobility. In large healthcare premises, especially those providing services for very highly dependent patients (such as those in intensive therapy units, special care baby units, and operating theatres) or disabled people, you may also need to consult a professional access consultant or take advice from disability organisations.†

Further guidance on people with special needs is given in Part 2, Section 1.15.

Checklist

- Have you identified who is at risk? ☐
- Have you identified why they are at risk? ☐
- Have you made a note of your findings? ☐

STEP 3   EVALUATE, REMOVE, REDUCE AND PROTECT FROM RISK

The management of the premises and the way people use it will have an effect on your evaluation of risk. Management may be your responsibility alone or there may be others, such as the building owners or managing agents, who also have responsibilities. Some premises may be part of a multi-use complex and all those with some control must co-operate and consider the risk generated by others in the building.

To maintain a pleasant healing environment and non-institutional atmosphere, precautions should be introduced carefully, taking account of any possible adverse effects on the quality of service users' lives and the care they receive.

---

* Visit the Disability Rights Commission website on www.drc-gb.org for more information.
† Further information can be found at www.drc-gb.org

3.1 Evaluate the risk of a fire occuring

The chances of a fire starting will be low if your premises has few ignition sources and combustible materials are kept away from them.

In general, fires start in one of three ways:

- accidentally, such as when smoking materials are not properly extinguished or when lighting displays are knocked over;

- by act or omission, such as when electrical office equipment is not properly maintained, or when waste packaging is allowed to accumulate near a heat source; or

- deliberately, such as an arson attack involving setting fire to external rubbish bins placed too close to the building.

Look critically at your premises and try to identify any accidents waiting to happen and any acts or omissions which might allow a fire to start. You should also look for any situation that may present an opportunity for an arsonist

Further guidance is given in Part 2, Section 1 on evaluating the risk of a fire starting.

3.2 Evaluate the risk to people

In Step 2 you identified the people likely to be at risk should a fire start anywhere in the premises and earlier in Step 3 you identified the chances of a fire occurring. It is unlikely that you will have concluded that there is no chance of a fire starting anywhere in your premises so you now need to evaluate the actual risk to those people should a fire start and spread from the various locations that you have identified.

While determining the possible incidents, you should also consider the likelihood of any particular incident; but be aware that some very unlikely incidents can put many people at risk.

To evaluate the risk to people in your premises, you will need to understand the the way fire can spread. Fire is spread by three methods:

- convection;

- conduction; and

- radiation.

Convection

Fire spread by convection is the most dangerous and causes the largest number of injuries and deaths. When fires start in enclosed spaces such as buildings, the smoke rising from the fire gets trapped by the ceiling and then spreads in all directions to form an ever-deepening layer over the entire room space. The smoke will pass through any holes or gaps in the walls, ceiling and floor into other parts of the building. The heat from the fire gets trapped in the building and the temperature rises.

Conduction

Some materials, such as metal shutters and ducting, can absorb heat and transmit it to the next room, where it can set fire to combustible items that are in contact with the heated material.

Radiation

Radiation heats the air in the same way as an electric bar heater heats a room. Any material close to a fire will absorb the heat until the item starts to smoulder and then burn.

Smoke produced by a fire also contains toxic gases which are harmful to people. A fire in a building with modern fittings and materials generates smoke that is thick and black, obscures vision, causes great difficulty in breathing and can block the escape routes.

Figure 5: Smoke moving through a building

It is essential that the means of escape and other fire precautions are adequate to ensure that everyone can make their escape to a place of total safety before the fire and its effects can trap them in the building.

In evaluating this risk to people you will need to consider situations such as:

• fire starting on a lower floor affecting the escape routes for people on upper floors or the only escape route for people with disabilities;

• fire developing in an unoccupied space that people have to pass by to escape from the building;

• fire or smoke spreading through a building via routes such as vertical shafts, service ducts, ventilation systems, poorly installed, poorly maintained or damaged walls, partitions and ceilings affecting people in remote areas;

• fire and smoke spreading through a building due to poor installation of fire precautions, e.g. incorrectly installed fire doors (see Appendix B2 for more information on fire doors) or incorrectly installed services penetrating fire walls; and

• fire and smoke spreading through the building due to poorly maintained and damaged fire doors or fire doors being wedged open.

Particular consideration should be given to fires that may start in non-patient access areas and affect adjacent patient access areas.

Where they suffer from limited mobility (or suffer claustrophobia), many patients in healthcare premises may wish (or need) to keep their bedroom doors open, for air or communications or comfort. Similarly, it can be of value to nurses (and patients) to have doors open so that the nurses can check the sleeping patients with a minimum of disturbance. A fire safety system should not impair the quality of treatment of the patients and the equipment provided and management procedures in place must be appropriate. In such cases, the use of 'hold-open' door devices should be considered (see Appendix B2).

Further guidance on fire risks is given in Part 2, Section 1.

3.3 Remove or reduce the hazards

Having identified the fire hazards in Step 1, you now need to remove those hazards if reasonably practicable to do so. If you cannot remove the hazards, you need to take reasonable steps to reduce them if you can. This is an essential part of fire risk assessment and as a priority this must take place before any other actions.

Ensure that any actions you take to remove or reduce fire hazards or risk are not substituted by other hazards or risks. For example, if you replace a flammable substance with a toxic or corrosive one, you must consider whether this might cause harm to people in other ways.

Remove or reduce sources of ignition

There are various ways that you can reduce the risk caused by potential sources of ignition, for example:

• Wherever possible replace a potential source by a safer alternative.

• Replace naked flame and radiant heaters with fixed convector heaters or a central heating system. Restrict the movement of and guard portable heating appliances.

• Operate a safe smoking policy in designated smoking areas and prohibit smoking elsewhere.

• Where smoking is permitted, provide sufficient and suitably placed ashtrays, bins of an approved type for the disposal of smoking materials.

• In dayrooms and other places where smoking is permitted, inspect every half hour and after they have been vacated at night to ensure that smokers' materials are removed and that they have not ignited other materials.

• Ensure electrical, mechanical and gas equipment is installed, used, maintained and protected in accordance with the manufacturer's instructions.

• Take precautions to avoid arson.

• Check all areas where hot work (e.g. welding) has been carried out to ensure that no ignition has taken place or any smouldering materials remain that may cause a fire.

• Ensure that no-one carrying out work on gas fittings which involves exposing pipes that contain or have contained flammable gas uses any source of ignition such as blow-lamps or hot-air guns.

Remove or reduce sources of fuel

There are various ways that you can reduce the risks caused by materials and substances which burn, for example:

• Reduce stocks of flammable materials, liquids and gases in patients' areas to a minimum. Keep remaining stock in dedicated storerooms or storage areas preferably outside where only the appropriate staff are allowed to go, and keep the minimum required for the operation of the premises.

• Ensure flammable materials, liquids and gases, are kept to a minimum, and are stored properly with adequate separation distances between them.

• Do not keep flammable solids, liquids and gases together.

• Remove, or treat large areas of highly combustible wall and ceiling linings, e.g. polystyrene or carpet tiles, to reduce the rate of flame spread across the surface.

• Develop a formal system for the control of combustible waste (including toxic and contaminated waste) by ensuring that waste materials and rubbish are not allowed to build up and are carefully stored until properly disposed of, particularly at the end of the day.

• Take action to avoid any parts of the premises, and in particular storage areas, being vulnerable to arson or vandalism.

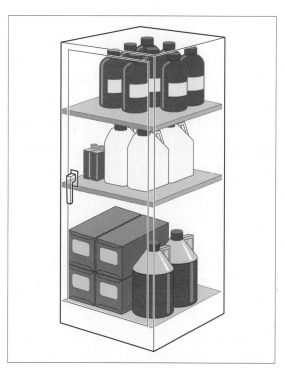

Figure 6: Storage of flammables

Remove or reduce sources of oxygen

You can reduce the potential source of oxygen supplied to a fire by:

• closing all doors, windows and other openings not required for ventilation, particularly when staff levels are low;

• shutting down ventilation systems which are not essential to the function of the premises;

• not storing oxidising materials near or with any heat source or flammable materials;

• controlling the use and storage of oxygen cylinders and/or piped oxygen, ensuring that they are not leaking; and

• maintaining piped oxygen supplies in accordance with the manufacturer's instructions.

Further guidance on removing and reducing hazards is given in Part 2, Section 1.

3.4   Remove or reduce the risks to people

Having evaluated and addressed the the risk of fire occuring and the risk to people (preventive measures) it is unlikely that you will be able to conclude that no risk remains of fire starting and presenting a risk to people in your premises.

You now need to reduce any remaining fire risk to people to as low as reasonably practicable, by ensuring that adequate fire precautions are in place to warn people in the event of a fire and allow them to escape safely.

The rest of this step describes the fire protection measures you may wish to adopt to reduce the remaining fire risk to people (see Steps 3.4.1 to 3.4.6).

The level of fire protection you need to provide will depend on the level of risk that remains in the premises after you have removed or reduced the hazards and risks. Part 2, Section 4.1 can help you decide the level of risk that you may still have.

Flexibility of fire protection measures

Flexibility will be required when applying this guidance, the level of fire protection should be proportional to the risk posed to the safety of the people in the premises. Therefore, the objective should be to reduce the remaining risk to a level as low as reasonably practicable. The higher the risk of fire and risk to life, the higher the standards of fire protection will need to be.

Your premises may not exactly fit the solutions suggested in this guide and they may need to be applied in a flexible manner without compromising the safety of the occupants.

For example, if the travel distance is in excess of that in Part 2, Table 2 on page 78, it may be necessary to do any one or a combination of the following to compensate:

• Provide earlier warning of fire using automatic fire smoke detection.

• Revise the layout to reduce travel distances.

• Reduce the fire risk by removing or reducing combustible materials and/or ignition sources.

• Control the number of people in the premises.

• Limit the area to trained staff only (no public).

• Increase staff training and education.

Note: The above list is not exhaustive and is only used to illustrate some examples of trade-offs to provide safe premises.

If you decide to significantly vary away from the benchmarks in this guidance then you should seek expert advice before doing so.

3.4.1 Fire-detection and warning systems

All healthcare premises will need some form of system for detecting fire and warning the occupants. Detection and warning of fire can be provided by staff and/or automatic fire-detection and warning systems.

In some small, single-storey open-plan premises, a fire may be obvious to everyone as soon as it starts. In these cases, where the number and position of exits and the travel distance to them is adequate, a simple shout of 'fire' or a simple manually operated device, such as a gong or air horn that can be heard by everybody when operated from any single point within the building, may be all that is needed. Where a simple shout or manually operated device is not adequate, it is likely that an electrical fire warning system will be required.

In larger premises, particularly those with more than one floor, where an alarm given from any single point is unlikely to be heard throughout the building, an electrical fire warning system incorporating sounders and manually operated call points (break-glass boxes) is likely to be required. This type of system will probably be acceptable in single occupancy premises where all parts are occupied simultaneously and it is unlikely that a fire could start without somebody noticing it quickly.

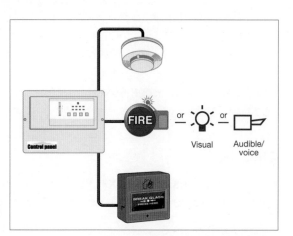

Figure 7: Fire-detection and warning system

However, in premises where there are significant unoccupied areas or common corridors and circulation spaces, particularly in more complex premises that are in multiple-use or multiple-occupation, where a fire could develop to the extent that escape routes could be affected before the fire is discovered, automatic fire detection is likely to be necessary.

You may need to consider special arrangements for times when people are working alone or when your normal occupancy patterns are different, e.g. when maintenance staff or other contractors are working in the building.

In larger multi-use healthcare premises, it is possible that a more sophisticated form of evacuation, e.g. phased evacuation or horizontal evacuation, will be used. In these cases it will be necessary for the fire-detection and warning system to automatically trigger the action that people need to take (in accordance with the pre-determined fire procedures). The warning system may also be based on voice alarms.

You need to consider how patients, in particular non-ambulant or semi-ambulant patients, should respond to an alarm. Patients who require staff assistance to make their escape can do little except wait for rescue and the sound of the alarm could be distressing. The sound level provided for patients then becomes of less significance. Communication procedures should be in place so that patients, who can hear the alarm but not respond, are notified as quickly as possible about what is happening.

It is of critical importance that staff know how to respond to an alarm and have well-rehearsed procedures in place.

If you have an electrical fire-detection and warning system, then it is desirable to have an alarm repeater panel at the building entrance and a means of briefing the fire and rescue service when they arrive.

False alarms from electrical fire warning systems are a major problem and result in many unwanted calls to the fire and rescue service every year. To help reduce the number of false alarms, the design and location of activation devices should be reviewed against the way the premises are currently used.

If you are not sure whether your current arrangements are adequate, see the additional guidance on fire-detection and warning systems in Part 2, Section 2.

Checklist

- Can the means of detection ensure a fire is discovered quickly enough for the alarm to be raised in time for all the occupants to escape safely? ☐

- Can the means of warning be clearly heard and understood by everyone throughout the relevant parts of the building when initiated from a single point? ☐

- If the fire-detection and warning system is electrically powered, does it have a back-up power supply? ☐

- Are the detectors of the right type and in the appropriate locations? ☐

3.4.2   Firefighting equipment and facilities

Firefighting equipment can reduce the risk of a small fire, e.g. a fire in a waste-paper bin, developing into a large one. The safe use of an appropriate fire extinguisher to control a fire in its early stages can also significantly reduce the risk to other people in the premises by allowing people to assist others who are at risk.

This equipment will need to comprise enough portable extinguishers that must be suitable for the risk.

In simple premises, having one or two portable extinguishers of the appropriate type, readily available for use, may be all that is necessary. In more complex premises, a number of portable extinguishers may be required and they should be sited in suitable locations, e.g. on the escape routes at each floor level. It may also be necessary to indicate the location of extinguishers by suitable signs

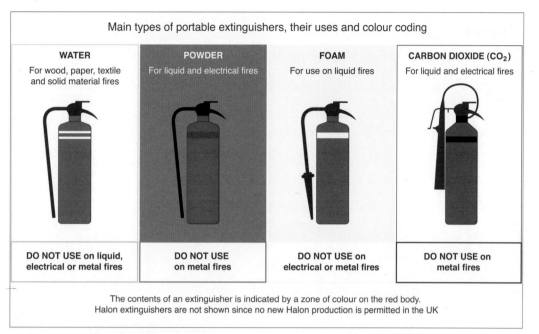

Figure 8: Types of fire extinguishers

Some premises will also have permanently installed firefighting equipment such as hose reels for use by trained staff or firefighters.

People with no training should not be expected to attempt to extinguish a fire. However, all staff should be familiar with the location and basic operating procedures for the equipment provided, in case they need to use it. If your fire strategy means that certain people, e.g. fire marshals, will be expected to take a more active role, then they should be provided with more comprehensive training.

Extinguishers should primarily be used to protect life and facilitate safe escape. They should otherwise only be used if they can be used safely and without risk of trapping the user.

Other fixed installations and facilities, such as dry rising mains, access for fire engines or automatically operated fixed fire suppression systems such sprinklers and gas or foam flooding systems, may also have been provided. Where these have been required by law, e.g. the Building Regulations or local Acts, such equipment and facilities must be maintained. Similarly, if provided for other reasons, e.g. insurance, it is good practice to ensure that they are properly maintained.

In most cases it will be necessary to consult a competent service engineer with regard to servicing and maintenance of these facilities. Keeping records of the maintenance carried out will help you demonstrate to the enforcing authority that you have complied with fire safety law.

Appendix A1 provides a sample fire safety maintenance checklist you can use.

For further guidance on portable fire extinguishers see Part 2, Section 3.1, for fixed firefighting installations, see Part 2, Section 3.2, and for other facilities (including those for firefighters) see Part 2, Section 3.3.

Checklist

- Are the extinguishers suitable for the purpose? ☐
- Have you taken steps to prevent the misuse of extinguishers? ☐
- Are there enough extinguishers sited throughout the premises at appropriate locations? ☐
- Are the right types of extinguishers located close to the fire hazards and can users get to them without exposing themselves to risk? ☐
- Are the extinguishers visible or does their position need indicating? ☐
- Do you regularly check any other equipment provided to help maintain the escape routes? ☐
- Do you carry out daily checks to ensure that there is clear access for fire engines? ☐
- Are those who test and maintain the equipment competent to do so? ☐
- Do you have the necessary procedures in place to maintain any facilities that have been provided for the safety of people in the building or for the use of firefighters, such as access for fire engines and firefighting lifts? ☐

3.4.3 Escape routes and strategies

Once a fire has started, been detected and a warning given, everyone in your premises should be able to escape safely, either unaided or with assistance, but without the help of the fire and rescue service. Where people with disabilities need assistance, staff will need to be designated for the purpose.

In all cases, escape routes should be designed to ensure, as far as possible, that any person confronted by fire anywhere in the building should be able to turn away from it and escape (or be evacuated), either direct to a place of total safety (single stage evacuaton) or initially to a place of reasonable safety (progressive horizontal or delayed evacuation), depending on the escape strategy adopted.

A place of reasonable safety can be a protected fire compartment (delayed evacuation) or an adjacent sub-compartment or compartment on the same level (progressive horizontal evacuation). From there, further escape should be possible either to another adjacent compartment, or to a protected stairway or direct to final exit.

The level of fire protection that should be given to escape routes will vary depending on the level of risk of fire within the premises and other related factors. Generally, premises that are simple, consisting of a single storey, will require fairly simple measures to protect the escape routes, compared with a large multi-storey building, which would require a more complex and inter-related system of fire precautions. Where occupants need assistance to evacuate, you must ensure that there are sufficient staff to ensure a speedy evacuation.

When determining whether your premises have adequate means of escape escape, you need to consider a number of factors, including:

- the type, number and dependency of people using the premises;

- assisted means of escape;

- the evacuation strategy;

- escape time and travel distance;

- the age, construction and size of the premises;

- the number of escape routes and exits;

- management of escape routes; and

- emergency eavcuation of people with mobility impairment.

The type, number and dependency of people using the premises

The people in your premises will primarily be a mixture of patients, staff and visitors.

Staff can reasonably be expected to have an understanding of the layout of the premises (or of the part in which they work), while visitors are unlikely to have knowledge of alternative escape routes. Patients may have limited knowledge, but will generally be guided or assisted to a place of safety by staff.

The number and dependency of people present will influence your assessment of the escape routes. You must ensure that your existing escape routes are sufficient and capable of safely evacuating all the people likely to use your premises at any time, particularly during busy times such as visiting hours. If necessary you may need either to increase the capacity of the escape routes, restrict the number of people in the premises or consider other safety measures (see Part 2, Section 4).

How quickly people can evacuate will depend on their level of reliance on staff, and it will therefore be helpful to consider the various categories of patient dependencies:

- **Independent**: the mobility of patients is not impaired in any way and they are able to physically leave the premises without the assistance of staff or, if they experience some mobility impairment, they are able to leave with minimal assistance from another person.

- **Dependent**: all patients except those defined as independent or very high dependency. This category also includes children and mental health patients regardless of their independent mobility.

- **Very high dependency**: those patients whose clinical treatment and/or condition create a high dependency on staff. This includes those in intensive care/intensive therapy units and operating theatres and those where evacuation would prove potentially life-threatening.

Assisted means of escape

Patients being cared for in healthcare premises will vary considerably in terms of mobility and levels of awareness during a fire situation. There may be patients who exhibit severe mobility restriction but will have a good awareness of the situation, being able to co-operate with staff. Others may exhibit normal mobility, but their level of awareness may be such that they present unpredictable behaviour (including violent behaviour), which may impede staff in an emergency. Patients with some forms of mental illness may become distressed by the alarm and the sudden activity. Some patients may not be fully ambulant or may be bedridden and dependent on medical equipment for their continued survival (for example in operating theatres and intensive care units) while others may have normal mobility and awareness (for example in outpatient clinics and GP surgeries).

In many cases, the evacuation of patients is likely to rely on the action of staff, guiding or moving them from the vicinity of the fire to an adjacent area providing reasonable safety.

The numbers of patients that may need to be moved in the event of a fire should be designed to be as few as possible. This may be achieved by establishing a number of protected areas within the premises. Restricting the number of patients within each protected area will be of benefit in an evacuation in terms of fewer patients requiring to be moved away from the fire.

You should ensure that staffing levels are both sufficient and available at all material times, to facilitate the movement of patients to a place of safety within the determined safe escape time (see below).

It is essential that your risk assessment takes full account of all difficulties that staff may encounter in moving people in an emergency. The conditions and dependency of patients, and hence their evacuation needs, can change over short periods of time. Therefore, it is important that staff play a part in the development of the emergency procedures. They will have a valuable contribution to make in terms of being aware of these changes, and be able to suggest any practical improvements to the evacuation procedure.

Evacuation strategy

You should not depend upon the fire and rescue service to evacuate people; your evacuation strategy must be dependent only on factors which are within your own control. However, you should consult with your enforcing authority when planning and determining an appropriate and effective evacuation strategy for your premises. Whichever system of evacuation you use must be supported by suitable management arrangements.

In healthcare premises, evacuation strategies are likely to fall into one or more of the following arrangements:

• single stage evacuation;

---

* See Part 2, Section 4.1 for the definition of a protected area.

- progressive horizontal evacuation; and

- delayed evacuation.

Single stage evacuation

This strategy is appropriate for healthcare premises where patients predominantly fall into the 'independent' category, where it may reasonably be expected that all people in the building are able to (and will) evacuate quickly out of the building to a place of total safety.

Progressive horizontal evacuation

This strategy is likely to be necessary where people are dependent on staff to assist with their escape. It works on the principle of moving the occupants from an area affected by fire, through a fire-resisting barrier to an adjoining area on the same level, where they can wait in a place of reasonable safety while the fire is dealt with, or await further evacuation to another similar area or, if necessary, down a protected route to total safety.

Delayed evacuation

In some parts of healthcare premises it may not be desirable or practical to evacuate some occupants immediately (e.g. because of medical conditions or treatments). In these circumstances, it may be appropriate to allow them to remain where they are while the fire is dealt with and the danger has passed, or to allow any additional time necessary to prepare them for evacuation (e.g. those in operating theatres, intensive care, etc.). In such circumstances it will be necessary to provide enhanced levels of structural fire protection to the individual room. However, where this strategy has been adopted, a suitable evacuation plan will still be required.

See Part 2, Section 4.1 for more information on evacuation strategies.

Escape time and travel distance

In the event of a fire, it is important to evacuate people as quickly as possible from the affected area or the building. Escape routes in a building should be designed so that people can escape quickly enough to ensure they are not placed in any danger from fire. The time available for escape will depend on a number of factors, including how quickly the fire is detected and the alarm raised, the number of available escape routes, the volume and height of the space, the ventilation conditions, the speed of fire growth, the mobility of the patients and adequate availability of staff. For simplicity, travel distances in Part 2, Table 2 on page 78 take these factors into account. Part 2, Section 4.1 provides additional guidance.

At the design stage of a building, the length of escape routes are kept within certain guidelines so that, in the event of a fire, the occupants can escape in the shortest time reasonably practicable.

The amount of escape time available will be closely linked to how quickly the staff are made aware of a fire within the premises, combined with the distances to be travelled.

For single stage evacuation strategies, where it would be expected that all the occupants would evacuate immediately, either to a place of reasonable safety inside the building e.g. aprotected stairway, or to a place of total safety outside the building, it is the time needed to reach these points which is measured. However, where progressive horizontal evacuation is adopted, the escape time is related to how long it takes to move patients from the area involved in fire, to a place of reasonable safety in an adjoining protected area on the same level (see Figure 22).

The time required to do this will be influenced by a number of factors, including:

• the degree of mobility of each patient to be moved;

• the level of awareness of each patient, and the level of co-operation that may be expected;

• the distance to be travelled to the adjoining protected area;

• the number of staff members available to move patients;

• the level of training given to staff in moving patients quickly in an emergency; and

• the need to disconnect any medical devices and to prepare the patient the patient for evacuation.

The ideal way to determine the actual time required would be to conduct a timed simulation involving the actual movement of all of the patients. This would identify many simple problems that may be rectified before any emergency evacuation should occur. However, as this is not practical in most cases, other methods should be developed for calculating escape time, including walking the escape routes (slowly) from all parts of the premises and then considering the number of patients needing staff assistance and the minimum number of staff on duty at any time.

The age and construction of the premises

Older buildings may comprise different construction materials from newer buildings, and may be in a poorer state of repair. The materials from which your premises are constructed and the quality of building work and state of repair could contribute to the speed with which any fire may spread, and potentially affect the escape routes the occupants will need to use. A fire starting in a building constructed mainly from combustible material will spread faster than one where fire-resisting construction materials have been used.

If you wish to construct internal partitions or walls in your premises, perhaps to divide up a recreation area, you should ensure that any new partition or wall does not obstruct any escape routes or fire exits, extend travel distances or reduce the sound levels of the fire alarm system. Any walls that affect the means of escape should be constructed of appropriate material.

Depending on the findings of your fire risk assessment, it may be necessary to protect the escape routes against fire and smoke by upgrading the construction of the floors, ceiling and walls to a fire-resisting standard. You should avoid having combustible wall and ceiling linings in your escape routes. Any structural alterations may require building regulation approval and you may need to seek advice from a competent person.

Further technical information on fire resisting construcion and wall and ceiling linings is provided in Appendix B.

If your premises have been purpose built for the provision of healthcare, and have been the subject of a fire risk assessment (such as HTM 86[80]) for this use in the past, it is likely that the level of structural protection present will be adequate.

However, the number and size of protected areas that are available to staff for evacuation purposes may need to be reviewed if circumstances within the premises change significantly. An example may be that the dependency of patients being cared for within the premises overall is increased, for example an out-patient clinic catering for the needs of fully ambulant patients in the past changes use to accommodate largely non-ambulant patients.

It is important that the correct balance is provided between adequate protection from fire and maintaining a comfortable and effective healing environment.

Figure 9:
A blocked corridor
with incorrect signage

The number of escape routes and exits

In general there should normally be at least two escape routes from all parts of the premises but in some small premises a single escape route may be acceptable in some circumstances (e.g. part of your premises accommodating less than 60 people) or where the travel distances are limited (see Part 2, Section 4).

Where more than one escape route is necessary and to further minimise the risk of people becoming trapped, you should ensure that the escape routes are completely independent of each other. This will prevent a fire affecting more than one escape route at the same time.

When evaluating escape routes, you may need to build in a safety factor by discounting the largest exit from your escape plan, then determine whether the remaining escape routes from a room, floor or building will be sufficient to evacuate all the occupants within a reasonable time. Escape routes that provide escape in a single direction only may need additional fire precautions to be regarded as adequate.

Exit doors on escape routes and final exit doors should normally open in the direction of travel, and be quickly and easily openable without the need for a key unless there are specific security reasons (e.g. medium secure or secure psychiatric premises – see also Part 2, Section 4: Means of escape – security). Checks should be made to ensure final exits are wide enough to accommodate the number and type of people (e.g. wheelchairs users) who may use the escape routes they serve.

Management of escape routes

It is essential that escape routes, and the means provided to ensure they are used safely, are managed and maintained to ensure that they remain usable and available at all times when the premises are occupied. Inform staff during training sessions about the escape routes within the premises.

Hospital streets, corridors and stairways that form part of escape routes should be kept clear and hazard free at all times. Items that may be a source of fuel or pose an ignition risk should not normally be located on any hospital street, corridor or in a protected stairway.

Closing doors

In wards or bedrooms designed to accommodate patients that are elderly or those with mental illness, the individual room may need to become a place of temporary safety for a period of time compatible with safe conditions remaining in the building (delayed evacuation). Although doors to these rooms are not normally required to be fitted with automatic self-closing devices, your emergency plan may require that staff immediately, on hearing the fire alarm, close all the doors in the building, in particular bedroom doors, to limit the growth of the fire, and to provide protection to patients. Alternatively, in other types of ward or bedroom, the doors could be on automatic closing devices which operate when the fire detection and warning system operates. After this, and only if (or while) it is safe, should evacuation be attempted. The rooms and their doors should have an appropriate level of fire resistance, and doors should be fitted with smoke seals (see Part 2, Section 4.1).

Emergency evacuation of persons with mobility impairment

The means of escape you provide must be suitable for the evacuation of everyone likely to be in your premises. This may require additional planning and allocation of staff roles – with appropriate training. Provisions for the emergency evacuation of disabled persons may include:

• stairways;

• evacuation lifts;

• firefighting lifts;

• horizontal evacuation;

• refuges;

• ramps; and

• suitable evacuation equipment.

Use of these facilities will need to be linked to effective management arrangements as part of your emergency plan. The plan should not rely on fire and rescue service involvement for it to be effective.

Further guidance on escape routes is given in Part 2, Section 4.

Checklist

• Is your building constructed, particularly in the case of multi-storey buildings, so that, if there is a fire, heat and smoke will not spread uncontrolled through the building to the extent that people are unable to use the escape routes? ☐

• Are any holes or gaps in fire-resisting walls, ceilings and floors properly sealed, e.g. where services such as ventilation ducts and electrical cables pass through them? ☐

• Are there an adequate number of protected areas? ☐

• Can all the occupants escape to a place of total safety in a reasonable time? ☐

• Are the existing escape routes adequate for the numbers and type of people that may need to use them, e.g. patients, visitors, and disabled people? ☐

• Have you made arrangements to ensure that all the escape routes within the building are properly maintained and available for use when required? ☐

• Are the exits in the right place and are they adequately protected, and lead as directly as possible to a place of total safety? ☐

• If there is a fire, could all available exits be affected or will at least one route from any part of the premises remain available? ☐

• Are the escape routes and final exits kept clear at all times? ☐

• Do the doors on escape routes open in the direction of escape? ☐

• Can all final exit doors be opened easily and immediately (other than secure environments) if there is an emergency? ☐

• Will everybody be able to safely use the escape routes from your premises? ☐

• Are your staff aware of the importance of maintaining the safety of the escape routes, e.g. by ensuring that fire doors are not wedged open and that combustible materials or obstructions are not stored within escape routes? ☐

• Are there any particular or unusual issues to consider? ☐

3.4.4 Emergency escape lighting

People in your premises must be able to find their way to a place of total safety if there is a fire by using escape routes that have enough lighting. Where any escape routes are internal and without windows or your premises are used during periods of darkness, including early darkness on winter days, some form of back-up to the normal escape route lighting should be provided.

In simple premises, e.g. a small single-storey GP surgery where the escape routes are straightforward, borrowed lighting, e.g. from street lamps where they illuminate escape routes, may be acceptable.

In most healthcare premises a more comprehensive system of automatic emergency escape lighting should be in place to illuminate all the escape routes.

In addition, where people have difficulty seeing conventional signs, a 'way guidance' system may need to be considered.

Further guidance on emergency escape lighting is given in Part 2, Section 5.

Checklist

- Is there sufficient lighting to safely use escape routes during periods of darkness? ☐

- Do you have emergency escape lighting to back up the normal lighting? ☐

3.4.5 Signs and notices

Signs

In some premises it is important to avoid an 'institutional' environment. However, signs must be used, where necessary, to help people identify escape routes, find firefighting equipment and emergency fire telephones. These signs are required under the Health and Safety (Safety Signs and Signals) Regulations 1996[5,6] and must comply with the provisions of those Regulations.

A fire risk assessment that determines that no escape signs are required (because, for example, trained staff will always be available to help members of the public to escape routes), is unlikely to be acceptable to an enforcing authority.

For a sign to comply with these Regulations it must be in pictogram form. The pictogram can be supplemented by text if this is considered necessary (see Figure 10) to make the sign more easily understood, but you must not have a safety sign that uses only text.

Where the locations of escape routes and firefighting equipment are readily apparent and the firefighting equipment is visible at all times, then signs are not necessary. In all other situations it is likely that the fire risk assessment will indicate that signs will be necessary.

Figure 10: Typical fire exit sign

Notices

Notices must be used, where necessary, to provide the following:

- instructions on how to use any fire safety equipment;

- the actions to be taken in the event of fire; and

- Information for the fire and rescue service (e.g. location of sprinkler valves or electrical cut-off switches).

All signs and notices should be positioned so that they can be easily seen and understood.

Figure 11: Simple fire action notice

Further guidance on safety signs and notices is given in Part 2, Section 6.

Checklist

- Where necessary are escape routes and exits, the locations of firefighting equipment and emergency fire telephones indicated by appropriate signs? ☐

- Have you provided notices such as those giving information on how to operate security devices on exit doors, those indicating doors enclosing fire hazards that must be kept shut and fire action notices for staff and other people? ☐

- Are you maintaining all the necessary signs and notices so that they continue to be correct, legible and understood? ☐

- Are you maintaining signs that you have provided for the information of the fire and rescue service, such as those indicating the location of water suppression stop valves and the storage of hazardous substances? ☐

3.4.6   Installation, testing and maintenance

New fire precautions should be installed by a competent person.

You must keep any existing equipment, devices or facilities that are provided in your premises for the safety of people, such as fire alarms, fire extinguishers, lighting, signs, fire exits and fire doors, in effective working order and maintain separating elements designed to prevent fire and smoke entering escape routes.

You must ensure regular checks, periodic servicing and maintenance are carried out whatever the size of your premises and any defects are put right as quickly as possible.

You, or a person you have nominated, can carry out certain checks and routine maintenance work. Further maintenance may need to be carried out by a competent service engineer. Where contractors are used, third party certification is one method where a reasonable assurance of quality of work and competence can be achieved (see Part 2, Section 8).

The following are examples of checks and tests that should be considered.

Daily checks

Remove bolts, padlocks and security devices from fire exits, ensure that doors on escape routes swing freely and close fully, and check exits and escape routes to ensure they are clear from obstructions and combustible materials, and in a good state of repair. Check the fire alarm panel to ensure the system is active and fully operational. Where practicable, visually check that emergency lighting units are in good repair and apparently working. Check that all safety signs and notices are legible. (See Appendix B3 for more details on bolts, padlocks and security devices.)

Weekly tests and checks

Test fire-detection and warning systems and manually-operated warning devices weekly following the manufacturer's or installer's instructions. Check that fire extinguishers and hose reels are correctly located and in apparent working order.

Monthly tests and checks

Test all emergency lighting systems to make sure they have enough charge and illumination according to the manufacturer's or supplier's instructions. Check that all fire doors are in good working order and closing correctly and that the frames and seals are intact.

Six-monthly tests and checks

A competent person should test and maintain the fire-detection and warning system.

Annual tests and checks

The emergency lighting and all firefighting equipment, fire alarms and other installed systems should be tested and maintained by a competent person. All structural fire protection and elements of fire compartmentation should be inspected and any remedial action carried out.

Appendix A1 provides an example of a fire safety maintenance checklist. You will find it of benefit to keep a log book of all maintenance and testing.

Further guidance on maintenance and testing on individual types of equipment and facilities can be found in the relevant sections in Part 2.

Checklist

- Do you regularly check all fire doors and escape routes and associated lighting and signs? ☐
- Do you regularly check all your firefighting equipment? ☐
- Do you regularly check your fire-detection and alarm equipment? ☐
- Are those who test and maintain the equipment competent to do so? ☐
- Do you keep a log book to record tests and maintenance? ☐

Step 3 Checklist

Evaluate, remove, reduce and protect from risks by:

- Evaluating the risk to people in your building if a fire starts ☐
- Removing or reducing the hazards that might cause a fire ☐

Have you:

- – Removed or reduced sources of ignition? ☐
- – Removed or reduced sources of fuel? ☐
- – Removed or reduced sources of air or oxygen? ☐

Have you removed or reduced the risks to people if a fire occurs by:

- – Considering the need for fire detection and for warning? ☐
- – Considering the need for firefighting equipment? ☐
- – Determining whether your escape routes are adequate? ☐
- – Determining whether your lighting and emergency lighting are adequate? ☐
- – Checking that you have adequate signs and notices? ☐
- – Regularly testing and maintaining safety equipment? ☐
- – Considering whether you need any other equipment or facilities? ☐

STEP 4   RECORD, PLAN, INFORM, INSTRUCT AND TRAIN

In Step 4 there are four further elements of the risk assessment you should focus on to address the management of fire safety in your premises. In some premises with simple layouts this could be done as part of the day-to-day management, however, as the premises or the organisation get larger it may be necessary for a formal structure and written policy to be developed. Further guidance on managing fire safety is given in Part 2, Section 7.

4.1   Record the significant findings and action taken

If your organisation employs five or more people, your premises are licensed, or an alterations notice requiring you to do so is in force, you must record the significant findings of your fire risk assessment and the actions you have taken.

Significant findings should include details of:

• The fire hazards you have identified (you don't need to include trivial things like a small tin of solvent-based glue).

• The actions you have taken or will take to remove or reduce the chance of a fire occurring (preventive measures).

• Persons who may be at risk, particularly those at greatest risk.

• The actions you have taken or will take to reduce the risk to people from the spread of fire and smoke (protective measures).

• The actions people need to take in case of fire including details of any persons nominated to carry out a particular function (your emergency plan).

• The information, instruction and training you have identified that people need and how it will be given.

For further information see Part 2.

You may also wish to record discussions you have had with staff or staff representatives (including trade unions).

Even where you are not required to record the significant findings, it is good practice to do so.

In some simple premises providing healthcare, record keeping may be no more than a few sheets of paper (possibly forming part of a health and safety folder), containing details of significant findings, any action taken and a copy of the emergency plan.

The record could take the form of a simple list which may or may not be supported by a simple plan of the premises.

In more complex premises, it is best to keep a dedicated record including details of significant findings, any action taken, a copy of the emergency plan, maintenance of fire-protection equipment and training. There is no one 'correct' format specified for this. Further guidance is given in Part 2, Section 7.1.

You must be able to satisfy the enforcing authority, if called upon to do so, that you have carried out a suitable and sufficient fire risk assessment. Keeping records will help you do this and will also form the basis of your subsequent reviews. If you keep records, you do not need to record all the details, only those that are significant and the action you have taken.

It can be helpful to include a simple line drawing to illustrate your fire precautions (see Figure 12). This can help you check your precautions as part of your ongoing review.

Figure 12: Example of a line drawing showing general fire safety precautions

The findings of your fire risk assessment will help you to develop your emergency plan, the instruction, information and training you need to provide, the co-operation and co-ordination arrangements you may need to have with other responsible people and the arrangements for maintenance and testing of the fire precautions. If you are required to record the significant findings of your fire risk assessment then these arrangements must also be recorded.

Further guidance about fire safety records with an example is given in Part 2, Section 7.1.

Checklist

- Have you recorded the significant findings of your assessment? ☐
- Have you recorded what you have done to remove or reduce the risk? ☐
- Are your records available for inspection by the enforcing authority? ☐

4.2 Emergency plans

You need to have an emergency plan for dealing with any fire situation.

The purpose of an emergency plan is to ensure that, where practicable, all the staff in your premises know what to do if there is a fire and that the premises can be safely evacuated.

If you or your organisation employ five or more people, or your premises are licensed or an alterations notice requiring it is in force, then details of your emergency plan must be recorded. Even if it is not required, it is good practice to keep a record.

Your emergency plan should be based on the outcome of your fire risk assessment and be available for your employees, their representatives (where appointed), patients (if they request it) and the enforcing authority.

In simple premises providing healthcare the emergency plan may be no more than a fire action notice.

In most premises providing healthcare, the emergency plan will need to be more detailed and, where necessary, compiled only after consultation with other occupiers and other responsible people, e.g. other occupiers in a multi-occupied building or others who have control over any part. In most cases this means a single emergency plan covering the whole building, and it will help if you can agree on one person to co-ordinate this task.

Further guidance on emergency plans is given in Part 2, Section 7.2.

Checklist

- Do you have an emergency plan and, where necessary, have you recorded the details? ☐
- Does your plan take account of other emergency plans applicable in the building? ☐
- Is the plan readily available for staff to read? ☐
- Is the emergency plan available to the enforcing authority? ☐

4.3 Inform, instruct, co-operate and co-ordinate

You must give clear and relevant information and appropriate instructions to your staff and the employers of other people working in your premises, such as contractors, about how to prevent fires and what they should do if there is a fire. In some premises you may also want to give information to patients and regular visitors.

All other relevant persons should be given information about the fire safety arrangements as soon as possible, e.g. contractors when they start work.

If you intend to employ a child, you must inform the parents of the significant risks you have identified and the precautions you have taken. You must also co-operate and co-ordinate with other responsible people who use or are connected to any part of the premises. It is unlikely that your emergency plan will work without this.

Information and instruction

All staff should be given information and instruction as soon as possible after they are appointed and regularly after that. Make sure you include staff who work outside normal working hours, such as contract cleaners or maintenance staff.

The information and instructions you give must be in a form that can be used and understood. They should take account of those with disabilities such as hearing or sight impairment, those with learning difficulties and those who do not use English as their first language.

The information and instruction you give should be based on your emergency plan and must include:

• the significant findings from your fire risk assessment;

• the measures that you have put in place to reduce the risk;

• what staff should do if there is a fire;

• the identity of people you have nominated with responsibilities for fire safety; and

• any special arrangements for serious and imminent danger to persons from fire.

In simple premises, where no significant risks have been identified and there are limited numbers of staff, information and instruction may simply involve an explanation of the fire procedures and how they are to be applied. This should include showing staff the fire-protection arrangements, including the designated escape routes, the location and operation of the fire-warning system and any other fire-safety equipment provided, such as fire extinguishers, and how to care for and evacuate patients. Fire action notices can complement this information and, where used, should be posted in prominent locations.

In most healthcare premises, written instructions should be provided to your staff who have been nominated to carry out a designated safety task, such as calling the fire and rescue service or checking that exit doors are available for use at the start of each shift.

Information about the premises should be readily available for the attending fire and rescue services. The information should be located at a pre-agreed location (usually the main entrance area). Information needed by fire crews about their construction, contents, hazards and built-in fire protection measures is becoming increasingly complex; the more information you can make available, the lower the risk to occupants, fire crews and, potentially, the premises.

Further guidance on information and instruction to staff, and on working with dangerous substances is given in Part 2, Section 7.3.

Co-operation and co-ordination

In premises that are not multi-occupied you are likely to be solely responsible. However, in buildings owned by someone else, or where there is more than one occupier, and others are responsible for different parts of the building, it is important that you liaise with them and inform them of any significant risks that you have identified. By liaising you can co-ordinate your resources to ensure that your actions and working practices do not place others at risk if there is a fire, and a co-ordinated emergency plan operates effectively.

Where two or more responsible persons share premises in which an explosive atmosphere may occur, the responsible person with overall responsibility for the premises must co-ordinate any measures necessary to protect everyone from any risk that may arise.

Employees also have a responsibility to co-operate with their employer so far as it is necessary to help the employer comply with any legal duty.

Further guidance on co-operation and co-ordination is given in Part 2, Section 7.3.

Checklist

- Have you told your staff about the emergency plan? ☐
- Have you identified people you have nominated to do a particular task? ☐
- Have you, where appropriate, told patients about the emergency plan? ☐
- Have you given staff information about any dangerous substances? ☐
- Do you have arrangements for informing temporary or agency staff? ☐
- Do you have arrangements for informing other employers whose staff are guest workers in your premises, such as maintenance contractors and cleaners? ☐
- Have you co-ordinated your fire safety arrangements with other responsible people in the building? ☐
- Have you recorded details of any information or instructions you have given and the details of any arrangements for co-operation and co-ordination with others? ☐

4.4   Fire safety training

You must provide adequate fire safety training for your staff. The type of training should be based on the particular features of your premises and should:

- take account of the findings of the fire risk assessment;
- explain your emergency procedures;
- take account of the work activity and explain the duties and responsibilities of staff;

- take place during their individual working hours and be repeated periodically where appropriate;

- be easily understandable by your staff and other people who may be present; and

- be tested by fire drills.

In simple premises this may be no more than showing new staff the fire exits and giving basic training on what to do if there is a fire. In complex premises, with a high staff turnover and many shift patterns, the organisation of fire safety training will need to be planned.

Your staff training should include the following:

- the importance of keeping fire-doors closed (or closing them) to prevent the spread of fire, heat and smoke;

- what to do on discovering a fire;

- how to raise the alarm and what happens then;

- what to do upon hearing the fire alarm;

- when to adopt a progressive horizontal evacuation;

- the procedures for alerting other staff, patients and visitors including, where appropriate, directing them to exits;

- the arrangements for calling the fire and rescue service;

- the evacuation procedures for everyone in your premises to reach an assembly point at a place of total safety, in particular the role of patients;

- the evacuation procedures for patients who require assisted escape, to reach an assembly point at a place of total safety;

- the location and, when appropriate, the use of firefighting equipment;

- the location of escape routes, especially those not in regular use;

- how to open all emergency exit doors;

- where appropriate, how to stop machines and processes and isolate power supplies in the event of a fire;

- the reason for not using lifts (except escape bed lifts or those specifically installed or nominated, following a suitable fire risk assessment, for the evacuation of people with a disability);

- the safe use of and risks from storing or working with highly flammable and explosive substances and bottled or piped oxygen;

- the importance of general fire safety, which includes good housekeeping; and

- fire drills, with and without patients' involvement.

All the staff identified in your emergency plan that have a supervisory role if there is a fire (e.g. heads of department, fire marshals or wardens and, in complex premises providing healthcare, fire parties or teams), should be given details of your fire risk assessment and receive additional training, and be aware of the importance of staff roles and staffing ratios.

Further guidance on fire safety training and examples of how to carry out a fire drill is given in Part 2, Section 7.4.

Checklist

- Have your staff received fire safety training? ☐
- Have you carried out a fire drill recently? ☐
- Are staff aware of specific tasks if there is a fire? ☐
- Are patients aware of specific actions if there is a fire? ☐
- Are you maintaining a record of training sessions? ☐
- If you use or store hazardous substances, have your staff received appropriate training? ☐

STEP 5 REVIEW

You should constantly monitor what you are doing to implement the fire risk assessment to assess how effectively the risk is being controlled.

If you have any reason to suspect that your fire risk assessment is no longer valid or there has been a significant change in your premises that has affected your fire precautions, you will need to review your assessment and if necessary revise it. Reasons for review could include:

- changes to work processes or the way that you organise them, including the introduction of new equipment;

- alterations to the building, including the internal layout;

- substantial changes to furniture and fixings;

- the introduction, change of use or increase in the storage of hazardous substances;

- the failure of fire precautions, e.g. fire-detection systems and alarm systems, life safety sprinklers or ventilation systems;

- significant changes to type and quantities of stock;

- a significant increase in the number of people present; and

- the presence of people with some different or specific form of disability.

You should consider the potential risk of any significant change before it is introduced. It is usually more effective to minimise a risk by, for example, ensuring adequate, appropriate storage space for an item before introducing it to your premises.

Do not amend your assessment for every trivial change, but if a change introduces new hazards you should consider them and, if significant, do whatever you need to do to keep the risks under control. In any case you should keep your assessment under review to make sure that the precautions are still working effectively. You may want to re-examine the fire prevention and protection measures at the same time as your health and safety assessment.

If a fire or 'near miss' occurs, this could indicate that your existing assessment may be inadequate and you should carry out a re-assessment. It is good practice to identify the cause of any incident and then review and, if necessary, revise your fire risk assessment in the light of this.

Records of testing, maintenance and training etc are useful aids in a review process. See Appendix A1 for an example.

Alterations notices

If you have been served with an 'alterations notice' check it to see whether you need to notify the enforcing authority about any changes you propose to make as a result of your review. If these changes include building work, you should also consult a building control body.

END OF PART 1

You should now have completed the five-step fire risk assessment process, using the additional information in Part 2 where necessary. In any review you may need to revisit Steps 1 to 4.

Part 2 Further guidance on fire risk assessment and fire precautions

Managing fire safety

Good management of fire safety in your premises is essential to ensure that any fire safety matters that arise are always effectively addressed. In small premises providing healthcare this can be achieved by the manager or owner maintaining and planning fire safety in conjunction with general health and safety.

In larger organisations it is good practice for a senior/board-level manager to have overall responsibility for fire safety. It may be appropriate for this responsibility to be placed with the manager designated with overall responsibility for health and safety.

An organisation's fire safety policy should follow the principles of HTM 05-01[82] and should be flexible enough to allow modification. This is particularly important when local managers have to function daily with other businesses in the same building. It should be recognised that fire safety operates at all levels within an organisation and therefore local managers should be able to develop, where necessary, a local action plan for their premises.

Some hospitals were not designed to be managed to these standards but were designed to conform to the principles of Nucleus fire precautions. There are seven main areas where Nucleus hospitals differ from other hospitals and these include management. For more information see Appendix E.

The organisation's policy should be set out in writing and may cover such things as:

- who will hold the responsibility for fire safety at board level;

- who will be the responsible person for each of their premises (this will often be the person who has overall control, usually the manager, but may be a number of duty or shift managers);

- means for ensuring that sufficient and adequately-trained staff are available at all times (day and night), to provide for the safe evacuation of patients from each area of the healthcare premises in accordance with the emergency plan;

- the arrangement whereby managers will, where necessary, nominate in writing specific people to carry out particular tasks if there is a fire; and

- the arrangement whereby regional or area managers should monitor and check that individual managers are meeting the requirements of the fire safety law.

You should have a plan of action to bring together all the features you have evaluated and noted from your fire risk assessment so that you can logically plan what needs to be done. It should not be confused with the emergency plan, which is a statement of what you will do if there is a fire.

The plan of action should include what you intend to do to reduce the hazards and risks you have identified and to implement the necessary protection measures.

You will need to prioritise these actions to ensure that any findings which identify people in immediate danger are dealt with straight away, e.g. unlocking fire exits. In other cases where people are not in immediate danger but action is still necessary, it may be acceptable to plan this over a period of time.

Before admitting the public to your premises you need to ensure that all of your fire safety provisions are in place and in working order, or, if not, that alternative arrangements are in place. Constant checks are needed while the public are present, and again after they have left. Detailed recommendations are given in BS 5588-12[58] and HTM 05-01.[82]

The guidance in Part 2 provides additional information to:

- ensure good fire safety management by helping you establish your fire prevention measures, fire precautions and fire safety procedures (systems equipment and plans); and

- assist you to carry out your fire safety risk assessment and identify any issues that need attention.

Section 1 Further guidance on fire risks and preventative measures

This section provides further information on evaluating the risk of a fire and its prevention in your premises. You should spend time developing long-term workable and effective strategies to reduce hazards and the risk of a fire starting. At its simplest this means separating flammable materials from ignition sources.

You should minimise fire hazards by considering:

- housekeeping;
- laundries;
- kitchen areas;
- storage;
- dangerous substances – storage, display and use;
- equipment and machinery;
- electrical safety;
- smoking; and
- managing building work and alterations.

You should minimise risk to people by considering:

- existing layout and construction;
- particular hazards in corridors and stairways used as escape routes;
- insulated core panels;
- restricting the spread of fire and smoke;
- arson;
- help for people with special needs; and
- lightning.

Some hospitals were not designed to HTM 81[76] but were designed to conform to the principles of Nucleus fire precautions. There are seven main areas where Nucleus hospitals differ from other hospitals and these include:

- management;
- fire and smoke containment;
- smoke dispersal; and
- separation of fire hazards.

For more information see Appendix E.

1.1 Housekeeping

For all healthcare premises, good housekeeping will lower the chances of a fire starting, so the accumulation of combustible materials in premises should be monitored carefully. Good housekeeping is essential to reduce the chances of escape routes and fire doors being blocked or obstructed.

Keep waste material in suitable containers before it is removed from the premises. If bins, particularly wheeled bins, are used outside, secure them in a compound to prevent them being moved to a position next to the building and set on fire. Never place skips against a building (see Figure 13) – they should normally be a minimum of 6m away from any part of the premises.

If you generate a considerable quantity of combustible waste material then you may need to develop a formal plan to manage this effectively.

In premises that provide healthcare, the predictable nature of the day-to-day activities should allow systems to be developed for dealing with waste, laundry and other combustible materials. However, such material should not be allowed to accumulate in the escape routes and this should form part of your considerations when carrying out the fire risk assessment.

Further information on housekeeping is available in HTM 83.[78]

Figure 13: Bins under stairway (courtesy of Cheshire fire and rescue service)

1.2 Laundries

Laundries, in both large and small healthcare premises, remain a high risk area. They are often located in the basement which means that any fire can affect the escape routes above.

Washing and drying machines should not be loaded in excess of the manufacturer's recommendations, exhaust filters should be cleaned and maintenance carried out regularly. Items such as cleaning cloths and mop heads placed in the dryers can spontaneously combust if there is any chemical residue left on them.

Ironing equipment should be correctly used and maintained. The laundry area should not be used for storing miscellaneous combustible material.

The use of laundry chutes in larger premises provides a ready path for smoke from any fire to travel throughout the patient access areas of the premises. Smoke and fire dampers within the laundry chute should be automatically operated following activation of fire-detection devices within the chute.

Further information on laundries is available in HTM 83.[78]

1.3 Kitchen areas

In larger premises with extensive catering facilities the cooking range should have some form of automatic fire suppression system. In smaller premises a suitable fire extinguisher and fire blanket should always be provided. All deep fat cooking equipment should have a thermostatic temperature control and should never be left unattended. The use of 'open top chip pans' should be discouraged or prohibited.

Extractor ducting, grease traps and filters should be regularly cleaned and maintained. Isolation switches for gas and electricity supplies, and any extractor fans should be located near an exit.

Further information on kitchens is available in HTM 83.[78]

1.4 Storage

Many of the materials found in your premises will be combustible. If your premises have inadequate or poorly managed storage areas then the risk of fire is likely to be increased (see Figure 14). The more combustible materials you store the greater the source of fuel for a fire. Poorly arranged storage could prevent equipment such as sprinklers working effectively.

In premises used for healthcare there can often be quite bulky combustible equipment, such as wheelchairs and bath chairs, which need to be stored away when not in use.

Combustible materials are not just those generally regarded as highly combustible, such as polystyrene, but all materials that will readily catch fire. Even non-combustible materials may present a fire hazard when packed in combustible materials. However, by carefully considering the type of material, the quantities kept and the storage arrangements, the risks can be significantly reduced.

Figure 14: An example of poor storage

In your office (if you have one), the retention of large quantities of paper records, especially if not filed away in proprietary cabinets, can increase the fire hazard. Such readily available flammable material makes the potential effect of arson more serious.

Many premises will take great care to present an efficient and attractive image in the areas used by patients and visitors, while storage areas are neglected and allowed to become dumping areas for unneeded material.

To reduce the risk, store excess materials and stock in a dedicated storage area, storeroom or cupboard. Do not store excess stock in areas where patients or visitors would normally have access.

Do not pile combustible material against electrical equipment or heaters, even if turned off for the summer, and do not allow smoking in areas where combustible materials are stored.

Your fire risk assessment should also consider any additional risk generated by seasonal products such as Christmas decorations.

Consider the following to reduce these risks:

- ensure electrical equipment in your store rooms does not become a potential source of ignition;

- provide adequate space for equipment, furniture and wheelchairs;

- allow storage in designated areas only;

- ensure storage areas are controlled and monitored; and

- provide separate storage areas for medical gases, aerosols and flammable gases (see below).

Voids

Voids (including roof voids) should not be used for the storage of combustible material. Such voids should be sealed off or kept entirely open to allow for easy access for inspection and the removal of combustible materials. Further guidance can be found in HTM 83.[78]

1.5 Dangerous substances: storage, display and use

Specific precautions are required when handling and storing dangerous substances to minimise the possibility of an incident. Your supplier should be able to provide detailed advice on safe storage and handling, however, the following principles will help you reduce the risk from fire:

- substitute highly flammable substances and materials with less flammable ones;

- reduce the quantity of dangerous substances to the smallest reasonable amount necessary for running the business or organisation;

- correctly store dangerous substances, e.g. in a fire-resisting enclosure. All flammable liquids and gases should ideally be locked away, especially when the premises are unoccupied, to reduce the chance of them being used in an arson attack; and

- ensure that you and your staff are aware of the fire risk the dangerous substances present and the precautions necessary to avoid danger.

Additional general fire precautions may be needed to take account of the additional risks that may be posed by the storage and use of these substances.

Certain substances and materials are, by their nature, highly flammable, oxidising or potentially explosive. These substances are controlled by other legislation in addition to fire safety law, in particular the Dangerous Substances and Explosive Atmospheres Regulations 2002[7] (also see HSE's *Approved Code of Practice and guidance*[8]).

Flammable liquids

Highly flammable liquids present a particularly high fire risk. For example, a leak from a container of flammable solvents, such as methylated spirit, will produce large quantities of heavier-than-air flammable vapours. These can travel large distances, increasing the likelihood of their reaching a source of ignition well away from the original leak, such as a basement containing heating plant and/or electrical equipment on automatic timers.

Flammable liquids stored in plastic containers can be a particular problem if involved in fire because they readily melt, spilling their contents and fuelling rapid fire growth.

The risk is reduced by ensuring the storage and use of highly flammable liquids is carefully managed, that materials contaminated with solvent are properly disposed of and, when not in use, they are safely stored. In individual rooms or areas up to 50 litres may be stored in a fire-resisting cabinet or bin that will contain any leaks (see Figure 16).

Quantities greater than 50 litres should be stored in a dedicated highly flammable liquids store.

Further guidance on the storage of highly flammable liquids in containers is available from the HSE.[74]

Figure 15: A fire-resisting pedal bin for rags

Figure 16: A 50 litre storage bin for flammables

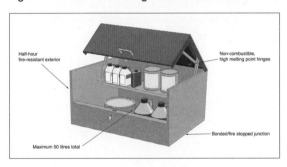

Half-hour
fire-resistant exterior

Non-combustible,
high melting point hinges

Maximum 50 litres total

Bonded/fire stopped junction

There should be no potential ignition sources in areas where flammable liquids are used or stored and flammable concentrations of vapours may be present. Any electrical equipment used in these areas, including fire alarm and emergency lighting systems, needs to be suitable for use in flammable atmospheres. In such situations, you should seek advice from a competent person.

LPG storage and use

LPG appliances and cylinders and in particular portable LPG equipment should only be used in exceptional circumstances. They should not be used or allowed in situations where they cannot be adequately and safely controlled. Nor should they be used where the use of mains gas is also prohibited.

Only butane cylinders should be used except when propane is required for building or maintenance work. Cylinders should not be used, or stored, in basements or cellars that have no natural floor-level ventilation.

Where it is necessary to keep spare butane cylinders they should be kept in a safe and secure place where they cannot be interfered with, that meets the following requirements:

- They should be kept upright and on a level base with the protective valve cap or plug fitted.

- They should not be located near any source of heat, source of ignition, or readily ignitible materials.

- They should not be kept near any corrosive, toxic or oxidant materials.

- They should be kept in a properly designed and located storage area that is dedicated for LPG.

Your supplier should be able to provide further guidance on the safe storage and use of LPG. Detailed advice is also given by the Liquefied Petroleum Gas Association.[9]

Advice on the use of LPG for heating is given below (Section 1.6).

Aerosols

Some aerosol cans contain flammable products stored at pressure and can present a high-level hazard. When ignited, they can explode, produce fireballs and rocket to distances of 40m. Their presence in premises can make it unsafe for firefighters to enter a building and they have the potential for starting multiple fires.

The following should be considered to reduce these risks:

- All staff involved in the movement, storage and display of aerosol cans should be adequately instructed, trained and supervised.

- Damaged and leaking aerosol cans should be removed immediately to a safe, secure well ventilated place prior to disposal. Powered vehicles should not be used to move damaged stock, unless specially adapted for use in flammable atmospheres. Arrangements should be made for safe disposal of aerosol cans at a licensed waste management facility.

- Stocks of aerosol cans should be segregated from other items, e.g. by use of caging. For larger quantities of aerosol cans a fire-resisting enclosure should be used.

- Cleaning and other staff should be made aware of the potential dangers of aerosol can and the need for safe disposal.

- Sprinkler protection.

Further guidance on the handling of aerosols is available from the British Aerosol Manufacturers' Association.[46]

Medical gases

The cylinders should be preferably stored outside, in a safe and secure location where they cannot be interfered with.

Where spare cylinders need to be stored indoors, the number should kept to the practical minimum and located in well ventilated areas, but not in passageways, stairwells or adjacent to emergency exits. Their location in designated marked cupboards or rooms provided with permanent ventilation to the outside is recommended.

Cylinders should:

- be kept away from extremes of heat, fires and naked lights (smoking should be prohibited in the vicinity);

- not be stored in areas where there is a possibility of their being contaminated with oils or greases, e.g. kitchen and garage areas;

- be secured to prevent them falling over; and

- be separated, full from empty cylinders, to avoid confusion.

Where medical gases are being used (either as piped supplies or in cylinders), guidance can be found in HTM 2022[83] or from the Medical and Healthcare Products Regulatory Agency (MHRA).*

The fire service should be informed if oxygen is used and stored on the premises.

Further advice on the safe use of medical oxygen systems is given by the European Industrial Gases Association.[47]

1.6 Equipment and machinery

General guidance on reducing ignition from work processes can be found in HTM 83.[78]

Lack of preventive maintenance increases the risk of fire starting in machinery. Common causes of fire in equipment and machinery are:

- allowing ventilation points to become clogged or blocked, causing overheating;

- poorly maintained equipment, such as residue accumulation in tumble driers;

- allowing extraction equipment in kitchens to build up excessive grease deposits;

- misuse or lack of maintenance of cooking equipment and appliances;

- loose drive belts or lack of lubrication leading to increased friction;

- disabling or interfering with automatic or manual safety features and cut-outs; or

- leaking valves, glands or joints allowing oils and other flammable liquids to contaminate adjacent floors or goods.

All equipment and machinery should be properly maintained by a competent person. Appropriate signs and instructions on safe use may be necessary.

In complex healthcare premises there should be:

- an effective programme of planned preventative maintenance in operation;

- an agreed proceedure for reporting faults;

- action once faults are reported to repair or make safe the equipment; and

- clear instruction provided for complex equipment.

Vehicles

There are hazards associated with industrial or mobility vehicles (e.g. wheelchairs or scooters), particularly during refuelling, recharging and maintenance operations, and also when stored or in use.

Battery charging of vehicles can give rise to sparks and hydrogen (a gas that is highly flammable, explosive and lighter than air). Sparks can occur when connecting and disconnecting power supplies.

Electric vehicle charging points should be carefully sited in a well ventilated area (ideally direct to open air), clear of ignition sources and preferably in a separate dedicated non-combustible structure. However, if sited in the building, the charging point should be against a fire-resting wall (e.g. 30 minutes' fire resistance).

Heating

There should be no need for individual heating appliances in most large or medium healthcare premises. However, if individual heating appliances are required, particularly for emergency use during a power cut or as supplementary heating during severe weather,

* www.mhra.gov.uk

care should be taken that they are used safely. The greatest risks arise from lack of maintenance and staff unfamiliarity with them. Heaters should preferably be secured in position when in use and fitted with a fire guard if appropriate.

As a general rule, convector or fan heaters should be preferred to radiant heaters because they present a lower risk of fire and injury.

The following rules should be observed:

- All heaters should be kept well clear of combustible materials and where they do not cause an obstruction.

- Portable fuel burning heaters (including LPG) should only be used in exceptional circumstances and if shown to be acceptable in your risk assessment.

All gas heating appliances should be used only in accordance with the manufacturer's instructions and should be serviced annually by a competent person.

Further information on equipment and machinery is available in HTM 83.[78]

1.7 Electrical safety

Electrical equipment is a significant cause of accidental fires in buildings. The main causes are:

- overheating cables and equipment due to overloading circuits;

- incorrect installation or use of equipment;

- damaged or inadequate insulation on cables or wiring;

- combustible materials being placed too close to electrical equipment which may give off heat even when operating normally or may become hot due to a fault;

- arcing or sparking by electrical equipment;

- overloading of sockets;

- incorrect fuse ratings; and

- little or no maintenance and testing of equipment.

Fans, including ventilation fans and hand dryers, should be regularly cleaned.

All electrical equipment should be installed and maintained in a safe manner by a competent person. If portable electrical equipment is used, including items brought into a workplace by employees, then your fire risk assessment should ensure that it is visually inspected and undergoes portable appliance testing ('PAT') at intervals suitable for the type of equipment and its frequency of use (refer to HSE guidance[10]). If you have any doubt about the safety of your electrical installation then you should consult a competent electrician.

Issues to consider include:

- correct fuse ratings;

- PAT testing and testing of the fixed installation;

- protection against overloading of installation;

- protection against short circuit;

- insulation, earthing and electrical isolation requirements;

- frequency of electrical inspection and test;

- temperature rating and mechanical strength of flexible cables;

- portable electrical equipment;

- physical environment in which the equipment is used (e.g. wet or dusty atmospheres); and

- use and maintenance of suitable personal protective equipment.

All electrical installations should be regularly inspected by a competent electrical engineer appointed by you, or on your behalf, in accordance with the Electricity at Work Regulations 1989 (EAW Regulations).[48] The use of low voltage equipment should conform to the requirements of the Electrical Equipment (Safety) Regulations 1994.[49]

Further information on electrical safety is available in HTM 83.[78]

1.8 Smoking

Carelessly discarded cigarettes and other smoking materials are a major cause of fire. A cigarette can smoulder for several hours, especially when surrounded by combustible material. Many fires are started several hours after the smoking materials have been emptied into waste bags and left for future disposal.

Consider prohibiting smoking in your premises other than in the designated smoking areas or smoking rooms. Display suitable signs throughout the premises informing people of the smoking policy and the locations where smoking is permitted. You should ensure that the smoking policy for staff, patients and guests is in place and enforced and prohibit smoking in fire hazard rooms and protected routes (e.g. lobbies, stairways).

In those areas where smoking is permitted, provide non-combustible deep and substantial ashtrays to help prevent unsuitable containers being used. Empty all ashtrays daily into a metal waste bin and take it outside. It is dangerous to empty ashtrays into plastic waste sacks which are then left inside for disposal later. In smoking-permitted areas, you should carry out inspections, particularly once these areas have been vacated at night.

1.9 Managing building work and alterations

Fires are more frequent when buildings are undergoing refurbishment or alteration.

You should ensure that, before any building work starts, you have reviewed the fire risk assessment and considered what additional dangers are likely to be introduced. You will need to evaluate the additional risks to people, particularly since your healthcare premises may continue to be occupied. Lack of pre-planning can lead to haphazard co-ordination of fire safety measures.

You should liaise and exchange information with contractors who will also have a duty under the Construction (Health, Safety and Welfare) Regulations 1996[11,12] to carry out a risk assessment and inform you of their significant findings and the preventive measures they may employ. This may be supported by the contractors' agreed work method statement. The designer should also have considered fire safety as part of the Construction (Design and Management) Regulations 1994 (the CDM Regulations).[50]

You should continuously monitor the impact of the building work on the general fire safety precautions, such as the increased risk from quantities of combustible materials and accumulated waste and maintaining adequate means of escape. You should only allow the minimum materials necessary for the work in hand within or adjacent to your building.

Additional risks that occur during building work can include:

- temporary electrical equipment;

- blocking of escape routes including external escape routes;

- introduction of combustibles into an escape route;

- loss of normal storage facilities;

- fire safety equipment such as automatic fire-detection systems becoming affected;

- fire-resisting partitions being breached or fire doors being wedged open (see Appendix B1 for information on fire-resisting separation); and

- additional personnel who may be unfamiliar with the premises.

Activities involving hot work such as welding, flame cutting, use of blow lamps or portable grinding equipment can pose a serious fire hazard and need to be strictly controlled when carried out in areas near flammable materials. This can be done by having a written permit to work for the people involved (whether they are your employees or those of the contractor).

The purpose of the permit is to ensure that the area is made as safe as possible before any hot working starts, that monitoring and precautions continue to be taken while the work is in progress, and that the area where the hot work was carried out and the surrounding area are monitored for at least an hour after completion of the work.

A permit to work is appropriate in situations of high hazard/risk and, for example, where there is a need to:

- ensure that there is a formal check confirming that a safe system of work is being followed;

- co-ordinate with other people or activities;

- provide time limits when it is safe to carry out the work; and

- provide specialised personal protective equipment, such as breathing apparatus, or methods of communication.

You must notify the fire and rescue service about alterations in your premises if an alterations notice is in force (see 'Who enforces the Fire Safety Order' on page 7).

Contractors should also be made aware of their obligations to maintain existing compartmentation, fire separation and stopping, and structural fire protection measures as far as is practicable or provide additional measures.

Further guidance on fire safety during construction work is available from the HSE[51, 52] and the Fire Protection Association.[53]

Further information on housekeeping is available in Section 1.1 and in HTM 83.[78]

1.10 Existing layout and construction

In many premises, the design is for open-plan areas, such as circulation areas, allowing patients and staff to move freely throughout the area.

Traditionally, occupants are advised to shut doors when escaping from a fire but in open-plan areas this is less effective. In these areas the fire, and especially the smoke, may spread faster than expected.

To assess the risk in your premises you need to evaluate the construction and layout of your building. This does not mean a structural survey, unless you suspect that the structure is damaged or any structural fire protection is missing or damaged, but rather an informed look around to see if there are any easy paths through which smoke and fire may spread and what you can do to stop that. In general, older buildings will have more void areas, possibly hidden from view, which will allow smoke and fire to spread away from its source. Whatever your type of building, you may need to consider typical situations that may assist the spread of fire and smoke such as:

- vertical shafts, e.g. lifts, open stairways, dumb waiters or holes for moving stock around;

- false ceilings, especially if they are not fire-stopped above walls;

- voids behind wall panelling;

- unsealed holes in fire-resisting walls and ceilings where pipe work, cables or other services have been installed; and

- doors, particularly to stairways, which are ill-fitting or routinely left open.

1.11 Particular hazards in corridors and stairways used as escape routes

Items that are a source of fuel, pose an ignition risk, or are combustible and likely to increase the fire loading should not be located on any corridor, stairway or circulation space that will be used as an escape route. Such items include:

- portable heaters, e.g. LPG or electric radiant heaters and electric convectors or boilers;

- gas cylinders for supplying heaters;

- cooking appliances; and

- some gas pipes, meters, and other fittings.

However, depending on the findings of your risk assessment and where more than one escape route is available, items such as those below may be acceptable if the minimum exit widths are maintained and the item presents a relatively low fire risk:

- non-combustible lockers;

- vending machines;

- small items of electrical equipment (e.g. photocopiers); and

- small quantities of upholstered furniture (which meet HTM 05-03 Part C[81]).

1.12 Insulated core panels

Some buildings used as healthcare premises, or as part of a healthcare premises, have insulated core panels as exterior cladding or for internal structures and partitions. Insulated core panels are easily constructed, which enables alterations and additional internal partitions to be erected with minimum disruption to business.

They normally consist of a central insulated core, sandwiched between an inner and outer metal skin. There is no air gap. The external surface is then normally coated with a PVC covering to improve weather resisance or the aesthetic appeal of the panel. The central core can be made of various insulating materials, ranging from virtually non-combustible through to highly combustible.

Figure 17: Insulated core panels – internal

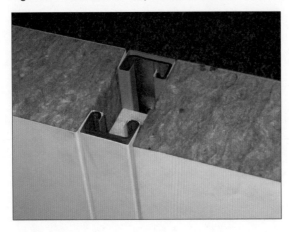

It is difficult to identify the type of core the panels have, therefore best practice can help you reduce any additional risk.

- Do not store highly combustible materials, or install heating appliances, such as baking ovens, against the panels.

- Control ignition sources that are adjacent to or penetrating the panels.

- Have damaged panels or sealed joints repaired immediately and make sure that jointing compounds or gaskets used around the edges of the panels are in good order.

- Check where openings have been made for doors, windows, cables and ducts that these have been effectively sealed and the inner core has not been exposed.

- Ensure there has been no mechanical damage and repair any that has occurred, e.g. caused by mobile equipment, such as wheelchairs.

- Ensure that any loads, such as storage and equipment, are only supported by panels which have been designed and installed to perform this function.

The panels should be installed by a competent person in accordance with industry guidance.[54]

The use of combustible panels in your premises should be carefully considered. Your fire risk assessment may need to be revised to ensure that any increased risk resulting from this type of construction is considered.

Further guidance on insulated core panels and the panel labelling scheme can be found in HTM 05-02: Part A.[76]

1.13 Restricting the spread of fire and smoke

To reduce the risk to people if there is a fire, you need to consider how to control or restrict the spread of fire and smoke. The majority of people who die in fires are overcome by the smoke and gases.

It is important ensure that, in the event of fire, the rate of fire growth is restricted in its early stages. It should also be noted that most measures which restrict the rate of fire growth in its early stages will also serve to restrict the fire spread in its later stages.

In practice, walls, particularly bedroom walls, are likely to be covered with a surface paint or wallpaper to provide a pleasant healing environment for the patient. Care is needed on the selection of decorative furnishes and multi-layer decorative systems, e.g. wallpapers and paints.

Further information on décor and surface finishes of walls, ceilings and escape routes is given in Appendix B.

Textiles and furniture

The use of flame-retardant bedding and furnishings will substantially reduce the fire risk.

You should ensure that curtains, drapes and other hanging textiles are inherently fire retardant or treated with a fire-retardant material.

On occasion, patients may provide items of their own clothing and furniture. Particular care should be taken to ensure that this does not introduce an additional risk.

For healthcare premises, guidance on textiles and furniture provided by the organisation (including at local level by managers) can be found in HTM 87.[81] Such items include:

- upholstered furniture;

- loose covers;

- textile fabrics for curtains (including nets, linings and blackout curtains);

- roller blinds; and

- textile floor coverings.

Polypropylene chairs should have flame-retardant polypropylene shells.

Totally soft play environments, although not furniture, can contain a large volume of foam in various shapes. Where such environments are extensive, as in gymnasia, extra care must be taken and additional precautions may be necessary.

If you have any doubts about the fire performance of any textiles or furniture, you could seek confirmation from the supplier that the items have been tested for flammability by a UKAS* accredited organisation. For healthcare premises providing treatment or care for dependent or very high dependency patients, the guidance in HTM 87[81] sets out appropriate standards to apply.

Bedding and sleepwear
Bedding and sleepwear supplied by the organisation should be resistant to ignition. Guidance on the fire performance of bedding and sleepwear can be found in HTM 87.[81] Such items include:

- blankets;
- counterpanes;
- continental quilts/duvets;
- mattresses;
- pillows; and
- sleepwear (including dressing gowns).

Pressure relief products
Many products such as mattress overlays, fleeces and underpads are used in the care of patients with, or with a pre-disposition to, pressure sores. They are usually used in conjunction with the bed assembly, or on easy chairs or wheelchairs. Where possible, these products should be resistant to ignition. Where this is not practicable, this should be recorded in the fire risk assessment.

Toys
The care and cleaning of any soft toys should be in accordance with the manufacturer's instructions in order to maintain the flame retardancy required under the Toys (Safety) Regulations 1989;[55] similarly, you should carefully check any soft toys donated to the premises to ensure that the flame retardancy requirements of the regulations are achieved.

If in doubt you should seek specialist advice about the treatments and tests for these materials, which can reduce their flammability and/or combustibility, or seek confirmation from the supplier that the items have been

tested for flammability by a UKAS* accredited organisation.

Fire-resisting structures
Many buildings are divided into different areas by fire-doors and fire resisting walls and floors. These are partly designed to keep a fire within one area, giving people more time to escape. You will need to identify which doors, walls and floors in your building are fire resisting. There may be information available from when the building was built, if alterations have been made, from fire plans, a previous fire risk assessment or from a previously held fire certificate.

High-risk areas (e.g. catering facilities) should be seperated from the rest of the premises by 30-minute fire-resisting construction.

Normally if there are fire doors in a wall, then the wall itself will also need to be fire resisting. (See Appendix B1 for more information about fire-resisting walls.) If a wall or floor is required to be fire resisting then you should not make any holes in it, e.g. for extra doors or pipe ducts, without consulting a competent person.

To ensure effective protection against fire, walls and floors providing fire separation must form a complete fire-resisting barrier, including any openings such as doors, ventilation ducts, pipe passages or refuse chutes.

The passing of services such as heating pipes or electrical cables through fire-resisting walls or partitions may leave gaps through which fire and smoke may spread. These should be rectified by suitable fire stopping and there are many proprietary products available for this purpose to suit particular types of construction. Such products should be installed by competent contractors.

In complex healthcare premises, such as hospitals and treatment centres, 30-minute fire-resisting barriers should be provided to sub-divide any concealed roof or ceiling void, so that the maximum area of uninterrupted roof or ceiling void should not exceed 400m².

Fire hazard rooms
Certain rooms, within patient access areas of healthcare premises, by their use constitute a particular fire hazard. Such rooms should be enclosed with fire-resisting construction and fire doors to ensure that they do not present a serious fire hazard to adjacent areas. Examples of fire hazard rooms and areas are listed in HTM 81[76] and include:

- store rooms;

- laboratories;

- lift motor rooms;

- bedrooms for elderly patients and those with mental illness;

- staff on-call rooms; and

- overnight rooms allocated for relatives.

With the exception of fire doors to patient bedrooms (single or multi-occupancy) provided for the elderly, those suffering from mental illness and those with learning difficulties, fire doors should be fitted with a self-closing device or kept locked shut when not in use (e.g. lift motor rooms). Those doors fitted with a self-closing device may incorporate a 'swing free' arm or electromagnetic hold-open device which is activated by the operation of the fire-detection and warning system.

Where self-closing devices are not fitted to fire doors, this should be taken into account in the ward fire safety management procedures. Further guidance can be found in HTM 05-01.[82]

Non-patient access areas

Fires may start in a non-patient access area and affect patients in an adjoining area. The following non-patient access areas should not be in the same compartment as patient access areas:

- boiler house;

- central sterile supply;

- central staff changing;

- commercial enterprises;

- flammable stores;

- hospital sterilising and disinfection unit;

- laundries;

- main electrical gear;

- main kitchens;

- main stores;

- medical gas store;

- medical records;

- pathology;

- patient services;

- pharmaceutical (manufacturing);

- refuse collection/disposal areas, incineration;

- staff on-call rooms; or

- works.

Smoke control

In healthcare buildings with atria or with fire-engineered solutions, there may be some form of smoke control provided for the safety of the occupants and to assist firefighting (e.g. Smoke and Heat Exhaust Ventilation Systems (SHEVS) or Pressure Differential Systems (PDS)). These systems are designed to restrict the spread of fire and smoke, usually by venting the heat and smoke through the roof or via other routes to the outside or by controlling the smoke movement via air pressure. Low level inlet air is essential for the operation of SHEVS and all openings for this purpose should not be obstructed.

Special downstands may have been installed to create a reservoir which will contain the smoke and hot gases at roof level, while vents allow the smoke to escape. It is important that any smoke can flow easily into the reservoirs and that nothing which could cause an obstruction, e.g. information display stands, are placed near the vents.

If your building has smoke vents fitted, or any other form of smoke control, then you may need to seek advice from someone who is competent in the design, installation and maintenance of such systems.

Further information on smoke control can be found from CIBSE Guide E[56] or from the BRE.[57]

Ventilation systems

Where ventilation systems might assist the spread of flames, smoke and hot gases from a fire, it will be necessary to take steps to safeguard the means of escape against this hazard. Ventilation ducts should be fitted with fire dampers (which close in the presence of fire) where they cross compartment boundaries (walls or floors) but may also need smoke dampers which operate on actuation of the alarm. In some premises, the dirty extract may continue to operate after the activation of the alarm, where it flows directly out of the building.

Further information can be found in HTM 81.[76]

1.14 Arson

Recent studies indicate that 25% of fires in healthcare premises are deliberately set. All premises can be targeted either deliberately or just because they offer easy access.

Be aware of other small, deliberately set fires in the locality, which can indicate an increased risk to your premises. Be suspicious of any small 'accidental' fires on the premises and investigate them fully and record your findings.

Fires started deliberately can be particularly dangerous because they generally develop much faster and may be intentionally started in escape routes. Of all the risk-reduction measures, the most benefit may come from efforts to reduce the threat from arson.

Measures to reduce arson may include the following:

- ensure the outside of the premises is well lit and, if practical, secure the perimeter of the premises;

- thoroughly secure all entry points to the premises, including windows and the roof, but make sure that any people working alone still have adequate escape routes;

- make sure you regularly remove all combustible rubbish;

- do not place rubbish skips adjacent to the building and secure waste bins in a compound separated from the building;

- encourage staff to report people acting suspiciously;

- remove automatic entry rights from staff who have been dismissed;

- ensure that your security alarm/fire-detection system is monitored and acted on;

- secure flammable liquids so that intruders cannot use them;

- fit secure metal letterboxes on the inside of letter flaps to contain any burning materials that may be pushed through;

- deter unauthorised entry to the site;

- prevent unauthorised entry into the building;

- reduce the opportunity for an offender to start a fire;

- reduce the opportunity for people with mental health/learning needs to start a fire;

- reduce the scope for potential fire damage;

- reduce the subsequent losses and disruption resulting from a fire by preparing a disaster recovery plan;

- maintain security of the main access door in the event of a fire; and

- recognise and resolve security/means of escape conflicts in premises providing accommodation for people with mental illness.

Healthcare premises should have a policy on the prevention of arson, which is specific to the challenge faced by each premises. Further guidance on the reducing the risk of arson has been published in HTM 05-03: Part F[85] and by the Arson Prevention Bureau.*

1.15 Help for people with special needs

Patients

By their nature, premises that provide healthcare will often have patients who have low mobility, alertness and/or responsiveness. Those particularly at risk include:

- those who cannot walk, either with or without assistance; and

- those who suffer from mental illness.

At even higher risk may be those whose clinical treatment and/or condition creates a high dependency on clinical staff, for example those in intensive care units, special care baby units and operating departments.

Ideally, very high dependency patients should not be placed in compartments adjoining non-patient access areas that contain significant fuel and/or ignition sources (see Section 1.13). Where it is not practicable to remove or reduce the risk, then additional fire precautions (e.g. automatic fire suppression in the compartment that poses the fire risk) will be required. For those who are highly dependent on staff, e.g. in intensive therapy units, it may be necessary to provide two hours' fire resistance to the walls and floors separating the compartment that poses the risk to patients, in addition to a full fire-detection or automatic suppression system installed in the risk area.

Other building occupants

In addition to healthcare patients who may require help in a fire emergency evacuation, there is also a need to consider other occupants of healthcare premises who are likely to need assistance in such an emergency. In taking into account these other building occupants, there is a need to consider any disabilities they may have and the impact on their ability to leave a building speedily in the event of fire or make them entirely dependent on others to escape.

The Disability Discrimination Act 1995

Patients or other occupants who are elderly, or very young, or in need of specialist care, may also have some other disability. The Disability Rights Commission estimates that 11 million people in this country have some form of disability. Owners and managers providing healthcare services will often have considerable experience in assisting disabled people to move about and they should carefully assess the practicalities of undertaking an emergency evacuation in the event of fire. If you have disabled employees you may also need to discuss their individual needs.

Under the Disability Discrimination Act 1995,[13] if disabled people could realistically expect to use the service you provide then you must anticipate any reasonable adjustments that would make it easier for that right to be exercised. Accordingly, if disabled people are going to be in your premises then you must also provide a safe means for them to leave if a fire occurs.

The Disability Discrimination Act includes the concept of 'reasonable adjustments' and this can be carried over into fire safety law. It can mean different things in different circumstances. For example, in a children's ward it may be considered reasonable to provide contrasting colours on a handrail to help those with vision impairment to follow an escape route more easily. However, it might be unreasonable to expect that same premises to install an expensive voice alarm system. Appropriate 'reasonable adjustments' for a large business or organisation may be much more significant.

In large premises with many severely disabled service users, you may also wish to contact a professional access consultant or take advice from disability organisations.

While the majority of disabled people wish to and are able to facilitate their own escape, there may be a significant number of people in premises that provide healthcare who are severely disabled and only able to move or react adequately with assistance from staff.

You may conclude that the current levels of assistance available in your premises and the layout and construction means that the evacuation of some people (most likely patients) cannot be guaranteed within an acceptable time. You will then need to introduce some additional method of ensuring their safety (e.g. an automatic fire suppression system) and you should seek specialist advice.

When disabled people (patients and employees, but also regular visitors) use the premises, their needs should be discussed with them. These will often be modest and may require only changes or modifications to existing procedures. You may need to develop individual 'personal emergency evacuation plans' (PEEPs) for disabled people who frequently use a building. They will need to be confident of any plan/PEEP that is put in place after consultation with them. As part of you consultation exercise you will need to consider the matter of personal dignity. If members of the public use your building then you may need to develop a range of standard PEEPs which can be provided on request to a disabled person or others with special needs.

Guidance on removing barriers to the everyday needs of disabled people is contained in BS 8300.[14] Much of this advice will also assist disabled people during an evacuation.

As discussed above, you should ensure that your emergency plan has a record of where disabled people are located in the building and includes a plan of action to assist them in the event of a fire.

Further advice can be obtained from the Disability Rights Commission at www.drc-gb.org.

1.16 Lightning

High-rise premises and those on high ground may be susceptible to lightning strikes. Large healthcare premises should be fitted with lightning protection in accordance with BS 6651[70] which gives guidance on the design of systems for the protection of structures against lightning, and all new systems should comply with its requirements. The design of lightning protection is specialised and advice should be taken from a suitably qualified person or installer on the specific protection required for each building.

All lightning protection systems should be visually inspected once in every 12-month period by a suitably qualified person and a record of inspections maintained.

Section 2 Further guidance on fire detection and warning systems

2.1 General principles

The primary purpose of a fire-detection and warning system is to alert staff, patients and occupants to enable them to move away from the fire to a place of safety while the escape routes are still clear of smoke.

Two means of detecting fires are used in healthcare premises: observation and automatic fire detection. HTM 81[76] and HTM 82[77] provide guidance on the detection of fire by observation and automatic means respectively.

Some hospitals were not designed to HTM 81[76] or HTM 05-02: Part A[76] but were designed to conform to the principles of Nucleus fire precautions. There are seven main areas where Nucleus hospitals differ from other hospitals and these include detection and alarm. For more information see Appendix E.

Observation by staff
In sleeping areas, the number of beds observable from the staff base is an important factor in detecting fires and should be maximised, consistent with patient privacy. In many hospital ward layouts it is typical to be able to observe between 30% and 60% of beds from the staff base.

The staff base is the location within the nursing management area from which all staff work, and where information is stored and exchanged. Although it is unlikely that the staff base will be permanently staffed, a location that provides good observation will improve the likelihood of a fire being detected at an early stage.

If, for any reason, your system fails, you must still ensure that staff and other people in your premises can be warned and escape safely. A temporary arrangement, such as whistles or air horns, combined with suitable training, may be acceptable for a short period pending system repairs.

Sound levels
The fire warning sound levels should be loud enough to alert everyone, taking into account background noise. In areas with high background noise, or where people may be wearing headphones or hearing protectors, the audible warning should be supplemented, e.g. with visual alarms. This is dependent on the clinical needs of the patients and in some areas the alarm will alert the staff only.

People with hearing difficulties
Where people have hearing difficulties, particularly those who are profoundly deaf, then simply hearing the fire warning is likely to be the major difficulty. If these persons are never alone while on the premises then this may not be a serious problem, as it would be reasonable for other occupants to let them know that the building should be evacuated. If a person with hearing difficulties is likely to be alone, then consider other means of raising the alarm. Among the most popular are visual beacons and vibrating devices or pagers that are linked to the existing fire alarm.

Voice alarms
Research has shown that some people do not always react quickly to a conventional fire alarm. Patients in your premises may include people, such as children, who react badly to the noise of an alarm. You may therefore wish to consider using a voice alarm that can also incorporate a public address facility. The message or messages sent must be carefully considered. However, it is essential to ensure that voice-alarm systems are designed and installed by a person with specialist knowledge of these systems.

Schematic plan
In order to quickly determine where a fire has been detected, you should consider displaying a schematic plan showing fire alarm zones in a multi-zoned system adjacent to the control panel.

2.2 Types of system

In most healthcare premises an electrical fire-detection and warning system will be necessary. The system should typically include the following:

- manual call points (break-glass call points) next to exits with at least one call point on each floor;

- electronic sirens or bells; and

- a control and indicator panel.

Exceptionally, in smaller healthcare premises without sleeping accommodation, such as dentists' and GPs' surgeries, a system of interconnected combined manual call points and sounders may be acceptable.

2.3 Manual call points

Manual call points, often known as 'break-glass' call points, enable a person who discovers a fire to immediately raise the alarm and warn other people in the premises of the danger.

People leaving a building because of a fire will normally leave by the way they entered. Consequently, manual call points are normally positioned at exits and storey exits that people may reasonably be expected to use in case of fire, not just those designated as fire exits. However, it is not necessary in every case to provide call points at every exit. You may wish to also locate some where they can be reached quickly by your staff.

Manual call points should normally be positioned so that, after all fixtures and fittings, machinery and stock are in place, no one should have to travel more than 45m to the nearest alarm point. This distance may need to be less if your premises cater for people of limited mobility or there are particularly hazardous areas. They should be conspicuous (red), fitted at a height of about 1.4m (or less for premises with a significant number of wheelchair users), and not in an area likely to be obstructed.

2.4 Automatic fire detection

Automatic fire detection provides the means for automatically detecting and warning of fire in the quickest possible time. It offers you the possibility of carrying out firefighting (because the fire is small) and the maximum period of time to implement your emergency plan and to evacuate patients, staff and other occupants.

In many healthcare premises, particularly those that are larger and more complex, an automatic fire-detection and warning system is likely to be necessary. Systems based on the detection of smoke, heat or carbon monoxide, or a combination of these, can be used.

The system should comply with HTM 82,[77] which provides general principles and technical guidance on the design, specification, installation, commissioning, testing, operation and maintenance of fire-detection and warning systems in hospitals and should be read in conjunction with BS 5839 Part 1.[16]

The system can be linked to other active fire safety systems in your building (e.g. door-closing devices and smoke control vents) so that they operate automatically.

Automatic fire detection is usually needed in the following areas:

- boiler rooms;

- laundries;

- kitchens;

- high-risk and unoccupied areas;

- storage areas and walk-in cupboards;

- large day rooms;

- access rooms to bedrooms; and

- bedrooms and areas or buildings served by a single stairway.

If your building has areas where a fire could develop undetected or where people work alone and might not see a fire, it may be necessary to check that your system protects these areas.

In smaller healthcare premises such as GP surgeries where automatic detection is considered necessary, a system based on interlinked self-contained smoke alarms may be acceptable.

The precise design and scope of the system required wil be subject to the findings of your fire risk assessment, advice from system engineers and guidance from appropriate standards.

2.5 Reducing false alarms

False alarms from automatic fire-detection systems are a major problem and result in many unwanted calls to the fire and rescue service every year. Guidance on reducing false alarms has been published in Fire Practice Note 11[86] and by DCLG/CFOA/BFPSA.[15]

If there are excessive false alarms in your premises, people may become complacent and not respond correctly to a warning of a real fire. In such circumstances, you may be failing to comply with fire safety law. All false alarms should be investigated to identify the cause of the problem and remedial action taken.

To help reduce the number of false alarms, the system design and location of detection and activation devices should be reviewed against the way the premises are currently used. For example, if a store room has been converted to a staff area with cooking facilities (e.g a microwave and toaster) then the likelihood of the detector being set off is increased. Consequently, subject to the outcome of the fire risk assessment, a heat detector may be more appropriate. Similarly, if a manual call point is placed in a storage area where there is continual movement of stock, the call point is likely to be accidentally damaged. In this case a simple, fabricated hinged metal guard around the call point is likely to solve the problem.

Occasionally people set off a manual call point in the genuine, but incorrect, belief that there is a fire. Nothing should be done to discourage such actions and the number of false alarms generated this way is not significant.

Further detailed guidance on reducing false alarms is available in BS 5839-1.[16]

2.6 Staged fire alarms

In many small healthcare premises the actuation of the fire-warning system should trigger the immediate and total evacuation of the building. However, in the majority of large or complex healthcare buildings this may not be necessary as alternative arrangements should be in place. Fire alarm arrangements for hospitals should comply with HTM 82.[77]

Alternative arrangements will include progressive evacuation where people potentially most at risk from a fire, usually those closest to where the alarm was activated, will be immediately evacuated, while others in the premises are given an alert signal and will only evacuate if it becomes necessary. Hospitals adopt this strategy of evacuation which allows for the progressive horizontal movement of people, from one fire compartment to another, away from the fire.

These arrangements require fire-detection and warning systems capable of giving staged alarms, including an 'alert signal' and a different 'evacuate signal', and should only be considered after consultation with specialist installers and, if necessary, the relevant enforcing authority.

Such systems also require a greater degree of management input to ensure that staff and others are familiar with the system and action required.

2.7 Testing and maintenance

Your fire-warning and/or detection system should be supervised by a named responsible person, given enough authority and training to manage all aspects of the routine testing and scrutiny of the system.

The control and indicating equipment should be checked at least every 24 hours to ensure there are no specific faults. All types of fire-warning systems should be tested once a week. For electrical systems a manual call point should be activated (using a different call point for each successive test), usually by inserting a dedicated test key (see Figure 18). This will check that the control equipment is capable of receiving a signal and, in turn, activating the warning alarms. Manual call points may be numbered to ensure they are sequentially tested.

Testing of the system should be carried out by a competent person.

It is good practice to test the alarm at the same time each week, but additional tests may be required to ensure that staff or people present at different times are given the opportunity to hear the alarm.

Where systems are connected to a central monitoring station, arrangements should be made prior to testing to avoid unwanted false alarms.

Six-monthly servicing and preventive maintenance should be carried out by a competent person with specialist knowledge of fire-warning and automatic detection systems. This task is normally fulfilled by entering into a service contract with a specialist fire alarm company.

It is good practice to record all tests, false alarms and any maintenance carried out.

Further guidance on testing and maintenance of fire-warning systems can be found in BS 5839-1.[16]

2.8 Guaranteed power supply

If your fire risk assessment concludes that an electrical fire-warning system is necessary, then the Health and Safety (Safety Signs and Signals) Regulations 1996[5, 6] requires it to have a back-up power supply as a fire alarm is a signal under these regulations.

Whatever back-up system is used, it should normally be capable of operating the fire-detection and warning system for a minimum period of 24 hours, and sounding the alarm signal in all areas for 30 minutes.

2.9 New and altered systems

Guidance on the design and the installation of new systems and those undergoing substantial alterations is given in the appropriate part of HTM 82[7] and BS 5839-1.[16] If you are unsure that your existing system is adequate you will need to consult a competent person.

Section 3 Further guidance on firefighting equipment and facilities

You have responsibility for the provision of appropriate firefighting equipment. It is also your responsibility to check that all firefighting equipment is in the correct position and in satisfactory, serviceable condition.

Appropriate staff should be trained in the use of all such equipment.

For firefighting equipment and facilities, most hospitals follow the guidance of HTM 81[76] and HTM 83.[78]

3.1 Portable firefighting equipment

Fires are classed according to what is burning. Fire extinguishers provided should be appropriate to the classes of fire found in your premises in accordance with Table 1.

Table 1: Class of fire

Class of fire	Description
Class A	Fires involving solid materials such as wood, paper or textiles.
Class B	Fires involving flammable liquids such as petrol, diesel or oils.
Class C	Fires involving gases.
Class D	Fires involving metals.
Class F	Fires involving cooking oils such as deep-fat fryers.

Note 1: If there is a possibility of a fire in your premises involving material in the shaded boxes then you should seek advice from a competent person.

Note 2: It is not safe to fight fires involving aerosols with fire extinguishers.

Number and type of extinguishers

Typically for the Class A fire risk, the provision of one correctly sized water-based extinguisher for approximately every 200m² of floor space, with a minimum of two extinguishers per floor, will normally be adequate.

Where it is determined that there are additionally other classes of fire risk, the appropriate type, number and size of extinguisher should be provided. Further information is available in BS 5306-8.[18]

Where the fire risk is not confined to a particular location, e.g. Class A fires, the fire extinguishers should be positioned on escape routes, close to the exit from the room or floor, or the final exit from the building. Similarly, where the particular fire risk is specifically located, e.g. flammable liquids, the appropriate fire extinguisher should be near to the hazard, so located that it can be safely used. They should be placed on a dedicated stand or hung on a wall at a convenient height so that employees can easily lift them off (at about 1m for larger extinguishers, 1.5m for smaller ones, to the level of the handle). Ideally no one should have to travel more than 30m to reach a fire extinguisher. If there is a risk of malicious use you may need to use alternative, and more secure, locations.

Consider the implications of the Manual Handling Operations Regulations 1992[17] when selecting and siting firefighting equipment.

In self-contained small premises, multi-purpose extinguishers which can cover a range of risks may be appropriate. Depending on the outcome of your fire risk assessment, it may be possible to reduce this to one extinguisher in very small premises with a floor space of less than 90m².

Extinguishers manufactured to current standards (BS EN 3-7[3]) are predominately red but may have a colour-coded area, sited above or within the instructions, denoting the type of extinguisher. Most older extinguishers, manufactured to previous standards, have bodies painted entirely in a single colour which denotes the type of extinguisher. These older extinguishers remain acceptable until they are no longer serviceable. However, it is good practice to ensure that old and new style extinguishers are not mixed on the same floor of a building.

The following paragraphs describe the different types of extinguisher. The colour referred to is the colour of the extinguisher or the colour-coded area.

Water extinguishers (red)

This type of extinguisher can only be used on Class A fires. They allow the user to direct water onto a fire from a considerable distance. A 9-litre water extinguisher can be quite heavy and some water extinguishers with additives can achieve the same rating, although they are smaller and therefore considerably lighter. This type of extinguisher is not suitable for use on live electrical equipment.

Water extinguishers with additives (red)

This type of extinguisher is suitable for Class A fires. They can also be suitable for use on Class B fires and, where appropriate, this will be indicated on the extinguisher. They are generally more efficient than conventional water extinguishers.

Foam extinguishers (cream)

This type of extinguisher can be used on Class A or B fires and is particularly suited to extinguishing liquid fires such as petrol and diesel. They should not be used on free-flowing liquid fires unless the operator has been specially trained, as these have the potential to rapidly spread the fire to adjacent material. This type of extinguisher is not suitable for deep-fat fryers or chip pans.

Powder extinguishers (blue)

This type of extinguisher can be used on most classes of fire and achieve a good 'knock down' of the fire. They can be used on fires involving electrical equipment but will almost certainly render that equipment useless. Because they do not cool the fire appreciably it can re-ignite. Powder extinguishers can create a loss of visibility and may affect people who have breathing problems and are not generally suitable for confined spaces.

Carbon dioxide extinguishers (black)

This type of extinguisher is particularly suitable for fires involving electrical equipment as they will extinguish a fire without causing any further damage (except in the case of some electronic equipment, e.g. computers). As with all fires involving electrical equipment, the power should be disconnected if possible. These type also do not cool the fire appreciably, so it can re-ignite.

Class 'F' extinguishers

This type of extinguisher is mostly suitable for large kitchens with deep-fat fryers.

Selection, installation and maintenance of portable fire extinguishers

All portable fire extinguishers will require periodic inspection, maintenance and testing. Depending on local conditions such as the likelihood of vandalism or the environment where extinguishers are located, carry out brief checks to ensure that they remain serviceable. In normal conditions a monthly check should be enough. Maintenance by a competent person should be carried out annually.

New fire extinguishers should comply with BS EN 3-7.[73] Guidance on the selection and installation of fire extinguishers is given in BS 5306-8,[18] for maintenance in BS 5306-3,[19] and for colour-coding in BS 7863.[20]

Fire blankets

Fire blankets should be located in the vicinity of the fire hazard they are to be used on but in a position that can be safely accessed in the event of a fire. They are classified as either light duty or heavy duty. Light-duty fire blankets are suitable for dealing with small fires in containers of cooking oils or fats and fires involving clothing.

3.2 Fixed firefighting installations

These are firefighting systems which are normally installed within the structure of the building. They may already be provided in your premises or you may be considering them as a means of protecting some particularly dangerous or risk-critical area as part of your risk-reduction strategy.

Hose reels

Permanent hose reels (see Figure 19) installed in accordance with the relevant British Standard (BS EN 671-3: 2000[21]) provide an effective firefighting facility. They may offer an alternative, or be in addition to, portable firefighting equipment. A concern is that untrained people will stay and fight a fire when escape is the safest option. Where hose reels are installed, and your fire risk assessment expects relevant staff to use them in the initial stages of a fire, they should receive appropriate training.

Note: It is not safe to fight fires involving aerosols with hose reels.

Maintenance of hose reels includes visual checks for leaks and obvious damage and should be carried out regularly. More formal maintenance checks should be carried out at least annually by a competent person.

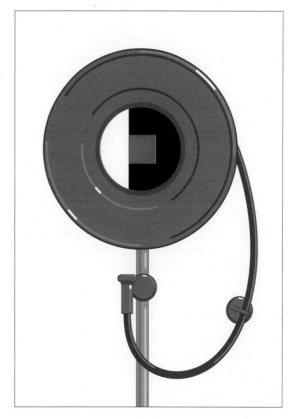

Figure 19: Hose reel

Sprinkler systems

Sprinkler systems can be very effective in controlling fires. They can be designed to protect life and/or property and may be regarded as a cost-effective solution for reducing the risks created by fire. Where installed, a sprinkler system is usually part of a package of fire precautions in a building and may form an integral part of the fire strategy for the building.

Sprinkler protection could give additional benefits, such as a reduction in the amount of portable firefighting equipment necessary, and the relaxation of restrictions in the design of buildings.

Guidance on the design and installation of new sprinkler systems and the maintenance of all systems is given in Loss Prevention Council (LPC) Rules, BS 5306-2[71] and BS EN 12845[22] and should only be carried out by a competent person.

Routine maintenance by on-site personnel may include checking of pressure gauges, alarm systems, water supplies, any anti-freezing devices and automatic booster pump(s). Diesel fire pumps should be given a test run for 30 minutes each week.

A competent maintenance contractor should provide guidance on what records need to be completed.

If a sprinkler system forms an integral part of your fire strategy it is imperative that adequate management procedures are in place to cater for those periods when the sprinkler system is not functional. This should form part of your emergency plan. Although the actual procedures will vary, such measures may include the following:

- Restore the system to full working order as soon as possible.

- Limit any planned shutdown to low-risk periods when numbers of people are at a minimum. This is particularly important when sprinklers are installed to a life safety standard or form part of the fire safety engineering requirements.

- You may need to isolate the area without the benefit of working sprinklers from the rest of the premises by fire-resisting material.

- Avoid higher-risk processes such as hot work.

- Extra staff should be trained and dedicated to conducting fire patrols.

- Any phased or staged evacuation strategy may need to be suspended. Evacuation should be immediate and complete. (Exercise caution as the stairways widths may have been designed for phased evacuation only.)

- Maintenance should be carried out on a zoned basis, to prevent leaving the whole system ineffective.

- Inform the local fire and rescue service.

If, having considered all possible measures, the risk is still unacceptable then, where appropriate, it may be necessary to consider closing all or part of the building. If in doubt you should seek advice from a competent person.

Other fixed installations
There are a number of other fixed installations including water mist, gaseous, deluge and fixed powder systems. If your premises have a fixed firefighting system that you are unfamiliar with, then seek advice. Where a fixed firefighting system forms an integral part of your fire safety strategy, it should be maintained in accordance with the relevant standard by a competent person.

3.3 Other facilities (including those for firefighters)

Building Regulations (HTM 81[76] or HTM 05-02: Part A[76]) and other Acts, including local Acts, may have required firefighting equipment and other facilities to be provided for the safety of people in the building and to help firefighters. Fire safety law places a duty on you to maintain such facilities in good working order and at all times.

These may include:

- access for fire engines and firefighters;

- . firefighting shafts and lifts;

- fire suppression systems, e.g. sprinklers, water mist and gaseous;

- smoke-control systems;

- dry or wet rising mains and firefighting inlets;

- information and communication arrangements, e.g. fire telephones and wireless systems and information to brief the fire and rescue service when they arrive; and

- firefighters' switches.

It may be appropriate to invite the fire and rescue service to familiarise themselves with layouts and fire systems, as a precautionary measure.

The Workplace (Health, Safety and Welfare) Regulations 1999[23] also require that systems provided for safety within a workplace are maintained.

Access for fire engines and firefighters
Buildings that have been constructed to modern building regulations (HTM 81[76] or HTM 05-02: Part A[76]) or in accordance with certain local Acts will have been provided with facilities that allow fire engines to approach and park within a reasonable distance so that firefighters can use their equipment without too much difficulty.

These facilities may consist of access roads to the building, hard standing areas for fire engines and access into the building for firefighters. It is essential that where such facilities are provided they are properly maintained and available for use at all relevant times.

Where a building is used by a number of different occupants you will need to ensure co-operation between the various 'responsible persons' to maintain fire and rescue service access. In exceptional cases, where access is persistently obstructed, you may need to make additional arrangements.

Generally, for large healthcare premises, access for the fire and rescue services should be provided to within 45m of 25% of the building perimeter. Access points into the building for firefighter personnel should be provided at suitable locations around the building. For multi-storey hospitals, at least one staircase suitable for use by firefighting personnel, which can be entered at ground level from a suitable access for a fire brigade appliance, should be provided.

Hospital roads used by firefighting appliances should be kept clear of obstructions at all times. If parking is allowed, sufficient safe clearance should be provided and maintained to allow firefighting appliances clear passage at all times. Fire and rescue service access should be indicated on site plans and any associated displays.

See Approved Document B to the Building Regulations[24] and HTM 81[76] for more information.

Firefighting shafts and lifts

Firefighting shafts (see Figure 20) are provided in larger buildings to help firefighters reach floors further away from the building's access point. They enable firefighting operations to start quickly and in comparative safety by providing a safe route from the point of entry to the floor where the fire has occurred.

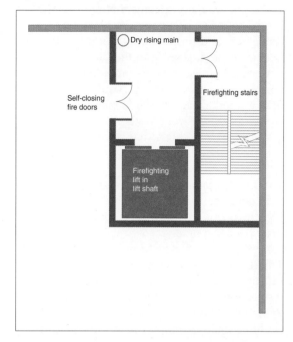

Figure 20: Fire fighting shaft

Entry points from a stairway in a firefighting shaft to a floor will be via a lobby, through two sets of fire and smoke-resisting doors and walls. Many people will use the stairway for normal movement through the building and it is important that the safety features are not compromised by doors being wedged open.

Most firefighting shafts will also incorporate a firefighting lift which opens into the lobby. The lift will have a back-up electrical supply and car control overrides. The primary function of the lift is to transport firefighting personnel and their equipment to the scene of a fire with the minimum amount of time and effort. It may also be used to help evacuate less mobile people.

Alterations that might affect the shaft should not be made without first liaising with other responsible persons, any owners or managing agents and the enforcing authority. Any proposed changes will require Building Regulation approval from a Building Control Body.

Where a firefighting shaft is provided, it should be maintained by a competent person.

Fire suppression systems

Fire suppression systems can include sprinklers and other types of fixed installations designed to automatically operate and suppress a fire. Such systems should be maintained by a competent person to a relevant standard.

Smoke control systems

These are complex systems that are provided for life safety of occupants, assistance to firefighters and property protection by clearing hot smoke and gases from the building. If you have one of these systems provided in your premises you should ensure you understand how it operates and that it is maintained in full working order. If your system is part of a larger system then you should liaise with other occupiers and building managers.

The smoke control system should be maintained by a competent person who is familiar with the fire engineering performance specifications of that specific system.

Where these systems are installed in addition to a sprinkler system, then the design and installation of each system should not act detrimentally on one another. A competent person should be employed to confirm this.

Dry and wet rising fire mains

The rising fire main (see Figure 21) is an important facility for the fire and rescue service in some healthcare premises, particularly in taller buildings. It consists of an inlet box where firefighters can connect their hoses, a pipe running up or through the building, outlet valves on each floor level and an air vent at the top.

It is important that fire mains remain in good working order. Issues to be considered can include the following:

- The physical approach to the inlet box should be such that a fire engine can park within 18m with the inlet box in view.

- Prohibit car parking in front of the inlet box.

- Secure the inlet box in such a way that firefighters can open the door without too much difficulty.

- It is advisable to lock the landing valves in the closed position, usually with a leather strap and padlock.

- Provide wet rising mains with a facility to allow the fire and rescue service to supplement the water supply.

Foam inlets

These special inlets are usually fitted to provide an efficient way of extinguishing a fire in a basement or other area of high risk such as a plant room. In many respects they look the same as rising main inlet boxes, but the door should be clearly marked 'foam inlet'. The risk area should be kept clear of obstructions to allow the foam to spread into the compartment.

Figure 21: Rising main

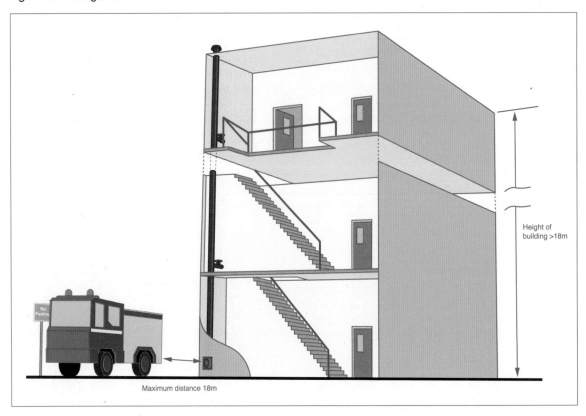

Maintenance of rising mains and foam inlets

All types of rising mains, foam inlets and associated valves should be maintained and tested on a regular basis by a competent person. Guidance on the inspection and testing of dry and wet rising mains is given in BS 5306-1.[72] Although there are no recommended periods between maintenance checks for foam inlets, it would be prudent to carry out an annual service.

Firefighters' switches

Luminous discharge lighting, e.g. neon signs, is occasionally used in healthcare premises for which this guide is intended. Safety switches are normally provided to isolate high-voltage luminous signs or to cut off electrical power. In the case of existing installations, if they have been provided in accordance with previous legislation (e.g. the Local Government (Miscellaneous Provisions) Act 1982[25]), then it is likely that they will comply with the Order.[1] If this is not the case, then you may need to consult the enforcing authority regarding the suitability of its location and marking. Testing should be carried out in accordance with the manufacturer's instructions. If you have no such instructions then an initial test should be carried out by a competent electrician.

Other firefighting facilities

As well as those already mentioned, other facilities to assist firefighters may have been installed in your premises and should be properly maintained by a competent person. Your maintenance audit (see Appendix A for an example checklist) should include these. Such facilities can include:

- information signs for firefighters;

- static water supplies, private hydrants, meter bypass valves and underground tanks;

- standby fire pumps, electrical generators, air pumps and hydraulic motors; and

- manual/self-closing devices for roller shutter doors in fire compartment walls.

Some hospitals were not designed to HTM 81[76] but were designed to conform to the principles of Nucleus fire precautions. There are seven main areas where Nucleus hospitals differ from other hospitals and these include firefighting provisions. For more information see Appendix E.

Section 4 Further guidance on escape routes and strategies

Introduction

This section provides further guidance on the general principles that apply to escape routes and strategies and provides examples of typical escape route solutions for a range of common building layouts. The guidance is based on the dependency of patients, which is defined in Part 1, Step 3.4.3 and in the Firecode suite of documents. You may have to adopt different solutions where your premises (or part of your premises) contain dependent or very high dependency patients.

You are not obliged to adopt any particular solution for escape routes in this guide if you prefer to meet the relevant requirement in some other way. If you decide to adopt some alternative arrangement it will need to achieve at least an equivalent level of fire safety.

You should be aware that some hospitals were not designed to HTM 81[76] but were designed to conform to the principles of Nucleus fire precautions. There are seven main areas where Nucleus hospitals differ from other hospitals and this includes means of escape. For more information, see Appendix E.

4.1 General principles

Evacuation strategies

Single stage evacuation (or independent)
Upon the activation of the fire alarm system, occupants should immediately leave the premises in accordance with the local fire policy and procedure arrangements. This strategy will be suitable for occupants who are unlikely to need assistance (e.g. independent patients) or where the premises are small and it is not possible or practical to provide adequate sub-compartments for use in conjunction with progressive horizontal evacuation (see below).

Progressive horizontal evacuation
Other than small healthcare facilities where patients can escape quickly and immediately to a place of total safety beyond the building, all other healthcare premises to which this guide applies should develop a strategy of progressive horizontal evacuation.

The principle of progressive horizontal evacuation is that of moving occupants from an area affected by fire through a fire-resisting barrier to an adjoining area on the same level, designed to protect the occupants from the immediate dangers of fire and smoke. The occupants may remain there until the fire is dealt with, or await further evacuation to another similar adjoining area or down the nearest protected stairway. This procedure should give sufficient time for non-ambulant and partially ambulant patients to be evacuated down stairways to a place of further (or total safety), should it become necessary to evacuate an entire storey (or the entire building). Progressive horizontal evacuation operates on the assumption of evacuation from compartment to compartment. The use of sub-compartments in progressive horizontal evacuation are to provide a temporary means of refuge to enable all those at risk to be evacuated promptly.

Figure 22: Protected areas in progressive horizontal evacuation

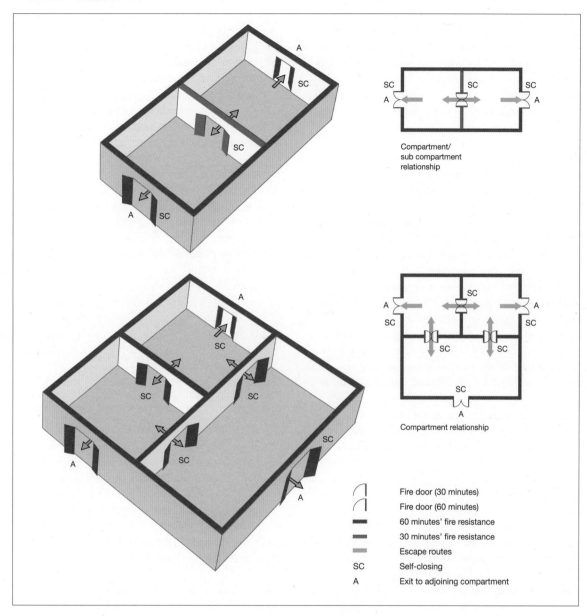

Compartment/sub compartment relationship

Compartment relationship

	Fire door (30 minutes)
	Fire door (60 minutes)
▬	60 minutes' fire resistance
▬	30 minutes' fire resistance
▬	Escape routes
SC	Self-closing
A	Exit to adjoining compartment

The number and size of the compartments and sub-compartments depends on a number of factors:

- the time it will take to evacuate people from the area of a fire to an adjacent protected area;

- the number of people to be evacuated;

- the level of any mobility impairment and co-operation;

- the number of staff to assist in evacuation; and

- the fire protection arrangements.

For healthcare premises designed to evacuate using progressive horizontal evacuation, the maximum size of a compartment should be 2,000m² (3,000m² in single-storey buildings). Compartments containing a department to which more than 30 patients have access at the same time or where there are more than 30 patient beds or trolleys, are usually provided with sub-compartmentation where the floor area is over 750m². For out-patient departments in hospitals and similar buildings (e.g. treatment centres), this floor area may be increased to 1,000m² before sub-compartmentation is required.

Each of the above factors will also influence the time needed to move the occupants from the fire area into the comparative safety of an adjoining protected area. A simple assessment can be made to determine the time more accurately by conducting a simulated evacuation exercise, involving patients, where safe to do so, or volunteers acting as patients. A reasonable 'worst case scenario' should always be assumed to give an accurate reflection of the longest time it would take to evacuate. This is usually when the lowest number of staff are available and where patients are more likely to require greater assistance (e.g. at night).

Evacuation should initially be a planned series of progressive horizontal moves to behind fire resisting barriers. It should therefore be possible to move from one compartment (or sub-compartment), to another compartment (or sub-compartment) capable of holding all those threatened, without a significant change in level, and from which there is the potential for further escape should that become necessary. Any evacuation should ensure suitable provision is made to enable treatment and care to continue.

There should be at least two separate compartments (or sub-compartments) on the each level, each of which has a minimum of two exits:

- one to an adjoining compartment or sub-compartment; and

- one to another adjoining compartment or sub-compartment, or to an exit stariway, or to the outside.

Each sub-compartment should provide 30 minutes fire-resistance and each compartment should provide at least 60 minutes fire resistance.

In a fire emergency, each compartment should be capable of accommodating, as well as its normal occupants, the designed occupancy of the most highly occupied adjoining.

Delayed evacuation
In some healthcare premises, generally those parts used for theatres, recovery, intensive care units, high dependency units and special care baby units, it may be difficult or dangerous (because of medical conditions or treatments) to get all semi-ambulant and non-ambulant patients into an adjoining protected area, or to a refuge during the intial stage of the evacuation. Other patients who may fit into this category will be identified by a specific

clinical assessment. In the above cases there will be a high staff to patient ratio.

In this situation, the individual suite or room may need to provide a temporary refuge to protect the occupants from a fire elsewhere in the building until they can be taken to a further place of safety (and if necessary to total safety), or until the danger has passed. This can be done by protecting the suite or room by enclosing it with fire-resisting construction.

A protected suite or room should be of at least 30 minutes fire-resisting construction and the door should be similarly fire-resising and normally fitted with a self-closing device. There are instances where for operational reasons self-closing devices are not fitted; in these cases staff should be instructed to close doors when an alarm is sounded. In addition the escape route from the protected suite or room to the adjoining protected areas, refuge or final exit (including any stairway) will also require an appropriate level of fire protection to allow access for staff to assist with subsequent evacuation. HTM 81[76] gives further guidance on the standards of fire resistance in protected areas.

If provision of such fire resistance is not possible, you may be able to show through your risk assessment that alternative measures to limit growth and spread of the fire are appropriate. Such measures might include for example automatic fire suppression system supported by robust staff response procedures. Such situations will be very rare and will need close scrutiny by a competent person.

Any patient who is initially left in a fire protected suite or room should ideally be accompanied by a member of staff who, in most cases, will already be in attendance at the time the alarm is sounded. The number of staff present will already have been determined by the clinical needs of the patient.

Other staff will know which rooms have been evacuated and those which still contain patients and where necessary are able to notify the fire and rescue service when they arrive.

Arrangements for delayed evacuation should only be based on a pre-planned basis, and the plan should involve clinical advice and decision making.

Communication procedures should let patients, who can hear an alarm but are not able to respond, know what is happening.

Whichever stategy or combination of evacuation strategies you adopt it is likely to be influenced by a number of factors including:

- size, type, layout and construction of premises;

- time of the day;

- reaction, mobility and dependency of residents;

- a clinical assessment of the patient(s);

- number of staff; and

- nature and location of occupants, e.g. visitors, residents, ancillary staff etc;

It is essential that your evacuation strategy is fully detailed in your emergency plan and included in your staff training programme (see Part 2, Section 7).

Suitability of escape routes

You should ensure that your escape routes are:

- suitable;

- easily, safely and immediately usable at all relevant times;

- adequate for the number of people likely to use them;

- generally usable without passing through doors requiring a key or code to unlock;

- free from any obstructions, slip or trip hazards; and

- available for access by the emergency service.

All doors on escape routes should open in the direction of escape, be side-hung or pivoted and ideally fitted with a safety vision panel. This is particularly important if more than 60 people use them or they provide an exit from an area of high fire risk. Normally this leads to the use of double swing doors on corridors and Hospital Streets.

The dependency of patients (defined in Part 1, Step 3.4.3) will determine the appropriate fire evacuation strategy to be adopted, i.e single stage, progressive horizontal or delayed evacuation.

In many older premises escape routes will very likely be through corridors or interconnecting rooms leading to the final exit. These routes are vital to ensure the safe evacuation of the occupants. They must be wide enough for their purpose as well as ensuring that people using the corridors for evacuation are adequately protected from the effects of any fire outbreak.

When assessing the adequacy of corridors where movement is not by bed or trolley, you should consider the following:

- Escape corridors should, in general, have a width of approximately 1100mm. (This will provide sufficient width for wheelchair access.)

- The floor should not be inclined at a gradient steeper than 1 in 12 to the horizontal.

- Escape corridors over 12m in length that connect two or more storey exits should be subdivided by fire doors to ensure no undivided length of corridor is common to more than one storey exit. This will minimise the risk of more than one escape route being affected by the fire.

At the building design or proposed alteration stage, the anticipated length of the escape routes is kept within certain acceptable limits. In the case of healthcare premises this may not only be related to the length of the escape routes, but also the time taken for all the patients at risk to be evacuated to an adjoining area of reasonable safety. However, there will be other occupants of the premises, such as visitors and contractors, etc., who will rely on conventional escape routes and procedures to escape from the premises.

In general there should normally be at least two escape routes from all parts of the premises. A route providing escape in one direction only (dead end) can be acceptable provided travel distances are within those recommended in Table 2 on page 78.

Where escape routes include an external route, there should be routine inspection and maintenance of the external element to ensure they remain fit for use.

Fire-resisting construction

The type and age of construction are crucial factors to consider when assessing the adequacy of the existing escape routes. To ensure the safety of people it may be necessary to protect escape routes from the effects of a fire. In older premises (see Appendix C for more information on historic buildings) it is possible that the type of construction and materials used may not perform to current fire standards.

Also changes of occupier and refurbishment may have led to:

- cavities and voids being created, allowing the potential for a fire and smoke products to spread unseen;

- doors and hardware worn by age and movement being less likely to limit the spread of smoke;

- doors exposed to mechanical damage being less likely to limit the spread of smoke;

- damaged or lack of cavity barriers in modular construction; and

- breaches in fire compartment walls, floors and ceilings created by the installation of new services, e.g. computer cabling.

In small healthcare premises, the exit from a room may be directly into a stairway in the premises. Therefore, all doors opening into the stairway should be 30-minute fire-resisting and self-closing.

In larger healthcare premises (e.g. hospitals and treatment centres) a 'protected area' approach is adopted with sub-compartments, compartments and/or a Hospital Street. In other areas, where it is concluded that an escape route needs to be separated from the rest of the premises by fire-resisting construction, e.g. a dead-end corridor or protected stairway (see Figures 29 and 35), then you should ensure the following:

- Doors (including access hatches to cupboards, ducts and vertical shafts linking floors), walls, floors and ceilings protecting escape routes should be capable of resisting the passage of smoke and fire for a minimum period of 30 minutes.

- Where suspended or false ceilings are provided, the fire resistance should extend up to the floor slab level above. For means of escape purposes a 30-minute fire-resisting rating is normally enough. However, where the wall is a compartment wall, 60 minutes' fire resistance would be necessary.

- Cavity barriers, fire stopping and dampers in ducts are properly installed.

It may be necessary to upgrade the standard of construction of the floors, walls and ceilings to provide 60-minute fire-resisting construction to ensure the occupants of the premises can be evacuated to a place of reasonable safety within a safe time. This will be crucial when considering providing further protected areas.

In wards for elderly or mental health patients, each bedroom should be enclosed in 30-minute fire-resisting construction. Doors should be of a similar fire-resisting standard, but need not be self-closing (see Section 1.13).

The ability of patients to move freely within the premises should not be affected by any fire safety provision.

If your premises have been previously designed and used as a large healthcare facility (e.g. a hospital or treatment centre), then it is likely that the structure has been assessed and is considered satisfactory for progressive horizontal evacuation. Any removal or alteration of the structure may have a serious impact on the safety of patients and should only be done where a comprehensive assessment and consultation has been carried out.

If there is any doubt about the nature of the construction of your premises, ask for advice from a competent person.

Number of people using the premises

As your escape routes need to be adequate for the people likely to use them you will need to consider how many people, including staff, patients and visitors, may be present at any one time. Where premises have been designed to building regulations or Firecode HTM 81[76] (or HTM 85[79]) for providing healthcare, the number and width of escape routes and exits will normally be enough for the anticipated number of people using the building. In such buildings where the risk has changed or buildings were constructed before national building regulations, it is still necessary to confirm the provision.

Knowledge of visiting hours and working patterns will give an indication of the likely numbers of people who may be expected to be on the premises.

If you propose to make changes to the use or layout of the building which may increase the number of people, you should check the design capacity by referring to guidance given in the Building Regulations Approved Document B[24] or HTM 81: Part A.[76]

Staff numbers and patient beds

In most healthcare premises, staff are always present and are expected to play a role in evacuation. A fire occurring in a healthcare establishment that results in the need for any evacuation will usually involve members of staff to assist in the movement of patients away from the area of the fire to a place of safety. How this can be achieved will depend, to a large degree, on the mobility of the patients, how well they respond to the emergency situation and the level of co-operation they are able to give.

At night, this situation will be made more difficult by the fact that most patients will be sleeping, with the responses of some being further impaired by medication. In many healthcare premises it will not be practicable to carry out an immediate full evacuation and, in any case, this may be harmful to the patients.

The more staff available to move patients the shorter the escape times will be. The numbers of staff will need to be carefully assessed, so that a sufficient number are available at all times to ensure that evacuation of the sub-compartment can be completed safely in the time available.

In healthcare premises accommodating in-patients, there is generally a minimum number of two staff present at all times (in a ward containing up to 30 beds). To ensure that adequate numbers of staff are on duty and available at all times – during meal breaks, etc. – generally it is necessary to have additional staff above the minimum on duty. Where the number of patients in the department is higher, the minimum number of staff present at all times should generally be increased. In any case the number of staff on duty and available should always be sufficient to ensure that the emergency plan will work effectively. Guidance on staffing levels can be found in HTM 85.[79]

The patients in healthcare buildings often comprise mixed levels of mobility and it is essential that staff are trained to react promptly to the fire alarm, in order to maximise the time available for evacuation.

Further information on staff training can be found in Part 2, Section 7.

Facilities for those with mobility impairment

Effective fire escape management arrangements need to be put in place for disabled occupants in the premises. The following points should be considered:

- A refuge is a place of reasonable safety in which disabled people can wait either for an escape lift or for assistance up or down stairs (see Figure 23). Disabled people should not be left alone in a refuge area while awaiting assistance. Depending on the design and fire resistance of other elements, a refuge could be a lobby, corridor, part of a public area or stairway or an open space such as a flat roof, balcony or similar place which is sufficiently protected (or remote) from any fire risk, and provided with its own means of escape and a means of communication.

- Where refuges are provided, they should be enclosed in a fire-resisting structure which creates a protected escape route leading directly to a place of safety and should only be used in conjunction with effective management rescue arrangements. **Your fire evacuation strategy should not rely on the fire and rescue service rescuing people waiting in a refuge.**

In all premises, if your escape plan requires disabled people to move to a refuge then you should consider the following:

- Arrangements will still need to be made for people to reach a place of ultimate safety.

- The refuge or protected area must provide safety from fire for at least 30 minutes or longer depending on the outcomes of your assessment. The refuge or protected area should only be considered as an area of temporary safety.

- There should be sufficient room in the refuge area for all disabled people and other occupants. The space available for a wheelchair should be a minimum of 900mm x 1,400mm, but consideration should be given to the number of users and the actual size of the wheelchairs.

- Management procedures should be robust enough to ensure that the whereabouts of people waiting in a refuge or protected area is always known (e.g. via a communication system).

If your escape plan involves the manual movement of mobility-impaired people down stairways there are a number of issues you should consider:

- Staff will always need to be available, adequately trained, able and willing to assist.

- The process will need to be regularly practised.

- Movement down the stairs must not impede the escape of others.

The following points apply to additional/alternative evacuation stategies in all premises.

- If firefighting lifts (provided in healthcare buildings five or more storeys above ground or access level) are to be utilised for evacuation, this should be co-ordinated with the fire and rescue service as part of the pre-planned evacuation procedures.

- Normal lifts may be considered appropriate for fire evacuation purposes, subject to an adequate fire risk assessment and development of a suitable fire safety strategy by a competent person.

- Even where escape lifts (dedicated lifts for use in an emergency) are installed, there is always the possibility of failure of the lift. It should therefore be possible to gain access to a protected stairway from the refuge area (should conditions in the refuge become untenable). Further information on the use of escape lifts in healthcare premises can be found in HTM 05-03: Part E.[87]

- Evacuation strategies must consider how disabled people who use wheelchairs can be moved down stairs in an emergency, taking account of health and safety manual handling regulations in addition to considering the dignity and confidence of the disabled person.

- Stairlifts should not be used for emergency evacuation. Where they are installed in premises, they should not reduce the effective width of a stairway intended to be used as an emergency evacuation route.

- Where ramps are provided on any circulation or escape route, they should be constructed in accordance with Approved Document M.[59]

The level of understanding of some elderly or mentally ill patients during an emergency might be such that they may resist assistance from staff due to fear and confusion. It may take time to calm them down sufficiently for evacuation to take place with their co-operation. Sedation due to medication may impede evacuation as more members of staff may be required to move people with suppressed responses. In parts of healthcare premises where patients have such impediments the options to ensure quick evacuation are likely to involve either reducing the size of the protected area or increasing the number of staff.

Further guidance is available in BS 5588-8[64] and BS 5588-12.[58]

Figure 23: An example of a refuge

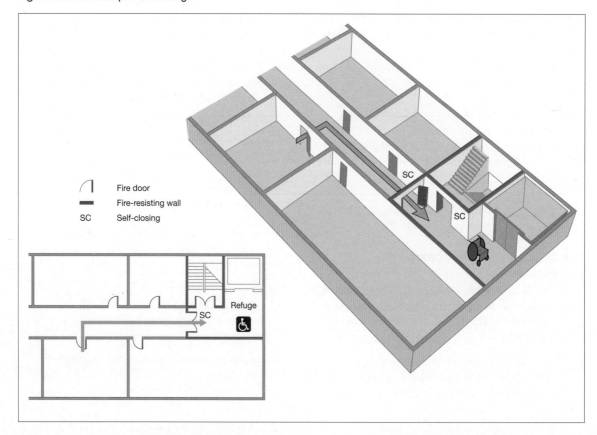

The responsibility to provide for the safe evacuation of all people in a building remains with the responsible person(s).

Fire protection arrangements

Having conducted a simulated evacuation of each protected area you should assess whether the evacuation times achieved are reasonable and consistent with those recommended for the levels of mobility likely to be found. If you conclude that movement times to an adjoining protected area are excessive then the following options should be considered:

- reducing the size of the protected area (this may be no more than dividing the building by positioning a set of fire-resisting self-closing doors across a corridor);

- providing additional staff to assist with the progressive horizontal evacuation;

- accommodating fewer people in the protected area; or

- providing additional fire protection systems, such as water suppression systems, to the protected areas in order to suppress fire growth.

Widths and capacity of escape routes and stairways

Once you have considered the number of people likely to be in the part of the premises, the next step is to establish that the capacity of the escape route is adequate for people to escape safely and in sufficient time to ensure their safety in the event of a fire.

The capacity route is determined by a number of factors including the width of the route, the time available for escape and the ability of the people using them.

At least two exits should be provided if a room/area is to be occupied by more than 60 persons. This number of 60 can be varied in proportion to the risk: for a lower risk there can be a slight increase, for a higher risk, lower numbers of persons should be allowed.

The effective usable width of an escape route is the narrowest point, normally a door or other restriction such as narrowing of a corridor due to fixtures and fittings. The effective width of a doorway is the clear unobstructed width through the doorway when the door is open at right angles to the frame. The effective width at any other point is the narrowest clear unobstructed width through which people can pass.

The capacity of an escape route is measured by the number of people per minute who can pass through it. Therefore, to establish the capacity of the exit, it will first be necessary to measure the width at the narrowest point.

For areas serving people with normal mobility (independent patients), the minimum width of an escape route in your premises should ideally be 1,100mm but in any case not less than 750mm (unless it is for use by less than five people in part of your premises).

Where the premises serve dependent and very high dependecy patients who are likely to be evacuated on beds or trolleys, the minimum width of the circulation route is usually 1,500mm, or, for a Hospital Street, a minimum 3,000mm wide. Door widths are naturally sized for bed or patient trolley use in progressive horizontal evacuation of patients.

In those departments and areas of large healthcare premises, where beds or patient trolleys will **not** be used, the minimum clear with of escape routes should be:

- for up to 200 people – 1,100mm;

- for over 200 people – an additional 275mm for every additional 50 people.

When calculating the overall available escape route capacity for premises that have more than one way out, you should normally assume that the widest is not available because it has been compromised by fire. If doors or other exits leading to escape routes are too close to one another, you should consider whether the fire could affect both at the same time (see Figure 26). If that is the case, it may be necessary to discount them both from your calculation.

Ideally, escape routes should have a clear height of not less than 2m except in doorways.

Travel distance

Having established the number and location of people in the building (or part of the building), you now need to confirm that the number and location of existing exits is adequate. This is normally determined by the distance people have to travel to reach them.

Table 2 gives guidance on travel distances. It should be understood that these distances should only be varied after seeking advice from a competent person.

In new buildings which have been designed and constructed in accordance with modern building standards the travel distances will already have been calculated. Once you have completed your fire risk assessment you need to confirm that those distances are still relevant.

When assessing travel distances you need to consider the actual distance to be travelled by people when escaping (eg allowing for walking around furniture, etc.). The distance should be measured from all parts of the premises to the nearest place of reasonable safety, which is:

- a protected stairway enclosure (a storey exit);

- a separate fire compartment or sub-compartment from which further escape can be made; or

- the nearest available final exit.

The distance to be travelled should be kept to as short as practicable as increased distances will inevitably mean extended escape times. Introducing more protected areas within the building may reduce travel distances, but this may seriously impact on the functional use of the premises, and should only be considered after other options have been explored.

The distance for initial horizontal movement suggested in Table 2 below should always be applied, based on the assessment of needs and mobility of the patients and the number of staff available.

These distances are based on those in HTM 81.[76]

Healthcare premises that have been built to building regulations (HTM 81[76] or HTM 05-02: Part A[76]) will usually have been provided with escape routes and maximum distances of travel in accordance with those set out in Table 2 (also see Figure 24). When assessing the distances of travel in higher risk areas, you should consider reducing the travel distances; this may need to be as much as a half to two-thirds of those suggested.

Although acceptable travel distances are suggested in Table 2 it must be emphasised that the time taken to move patients will be the important factor in any fire situation.

Table 2: Suggested travel distances

Escape routes	Suggested travel distances
Where more than one route is provided	30m in a sub-compartment (see Notes 1 and 3) 45m in a sub-compartment (see Notes 2 and 3)
Where only a single escape route is provided (see Note 4)	15m (see Note 1) 18m (see Note 2)
Total travel distance within a compartment	60m (see Note 3)

Note 1: This distance applies where patients are either dependent or very high dependency.

Note 2:- This distance applies where patients are independent.

Note 3: The total travel distance is measured from any point in the compartment (or sub-compartment) to the nearest exit.

Note 4: In some healthcare premises these travel distances in Table 2 will be exceeded for certain locations. Typically, these will be aespetic suites, operating departments and linac rooms. Extended travel distances should be clearly identified in fire risk assessments and fire strategy documents.

Measuring travel distance

When assessing travel distances, the route taken through a room or space will be determined by the layout of the contents, e.g. work stations, beds, furniture, etc. (see Figure 24). It is good practice to ensure routes are as direct and short as possible. When this is not possible, the direct line of travel may have to be reduced by one third to one half depending on the layout. The distances in Table 2 assume a direct line of travel.

Where the contents of rooms are liable to change, you should ensure that the exits from the room do not become inadvertantly blocked or the escape route significantly extended.

If in doubt about the travel distance, advice should be sought from a competent person.

Figure 24 illustrates an example how the travel distances as suggested in Table 2 should be applied.

Figure 24: Measuring travel distance

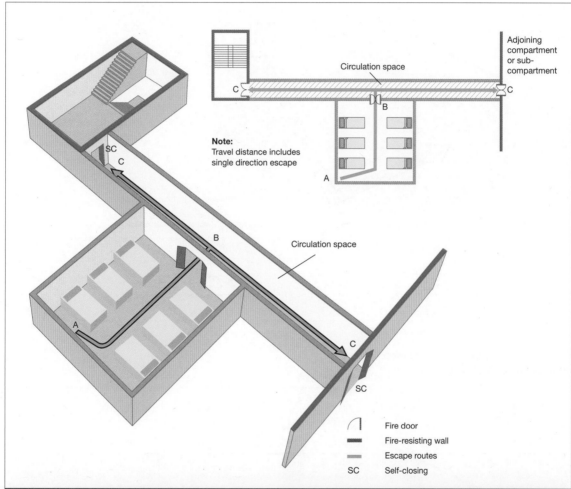

	Dependent or VHD patients		Independent patients	
	Sub-compartment	Compartment	Sub-compartment	Compartment
A – B	15m	15m	18m	18m
A – C (Measured to the nearest metre)	30m	60m	45m	60m

Alternative exits

Where alternative exits from a space or room are necessary they should, wherever possible, be located at least 45° apart (see Figure 25) unless the routes to them are separated by fire-resisting construction (see Figure 26). If in doubt consult a competent person.

Figure 25: Alternative exits

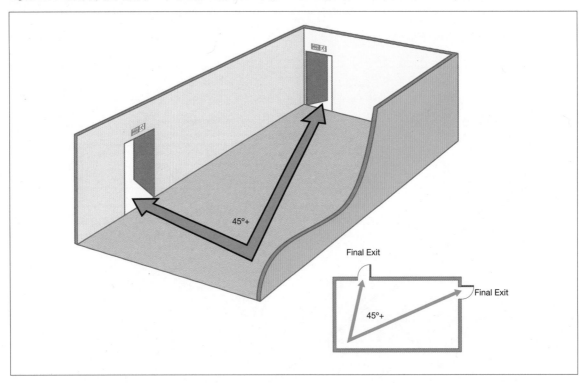

Figure 26: Alternative exits (separated by fire-resisting construction)

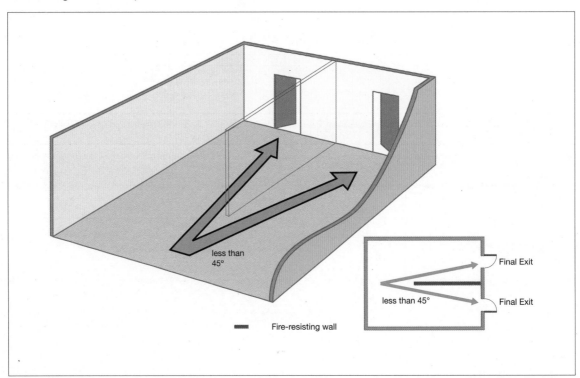

Inner rooms

Where the only way out of a room is through another room (see Figure 27), an unnoticed fire in the outer room could trap people in the inner room. This means of escape should be avoided where possible. If, however, avoiding this solution cannot be achieved then adequate warning of a fire should be provided by **any one** of the following means:

- a vision panel between the two rooms providing sufficient observation to give an indication of the conditions in the outer room and the means of escape;

- a large enough gap between the dividing wall and the ceiling, e.g. 500mm, so that smoke will be seen; or

- an automatic smoke detector in the outer room that will sound a warning in the inner room.

In addition, the following points should also be considered:

- avoid using an inner room as a bedroom.

- the outer room should not be a high fire risk area.

- restrict the number of people using an inner room to 30.

- ensure that outer rooms are under the control of the same person as the inner room.

- no one should have to pass through more than one access room when making their escape.

- the travel distance from any point in the inner room to the exit from the access room should be restricted to that for a single escape route (see Table 2 on page 78).

Figure 27: Inner rooms

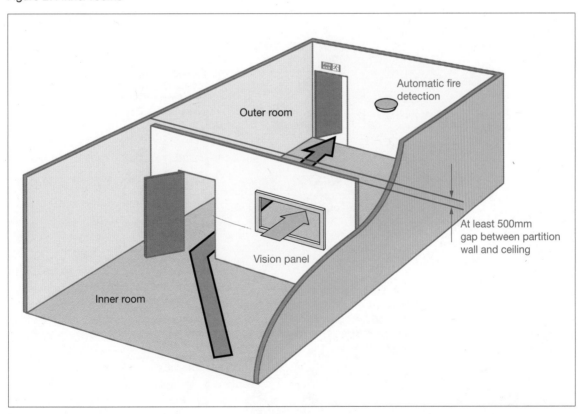

Outer room

Automatic fire detection

At least 500mm gap between partition wall and ceiling

Vision panel

Inner room

Measuring travel distances for initial dead-end travel

Where the initial direction of travel is in one direction only (see Figure 28, distance A–B), the travel distance should be limited to that for a single escape route in Table 2 on page 78.

Figure 28: Measuring travel distance for initial dead-end

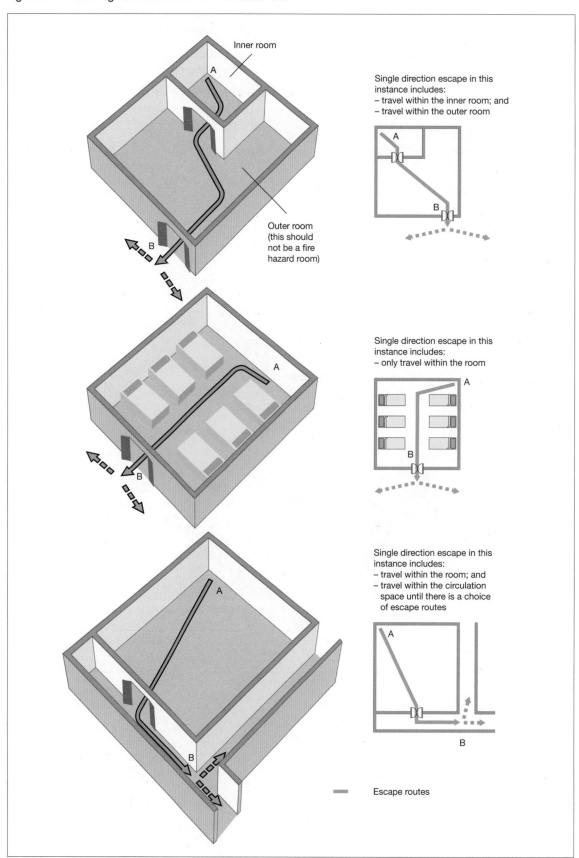

Escape routes with dead-end conditions

If your premises has areas from which escape can be made in one direction only (a dead end), then an undetected fire in that area could affect people trying to escape. To overcome this problem, limit the travel distance (see Table 2 on page 78) and use one of the following solutions:

- Fit an automatic fire-detection and warning system in those areas where a fire could present a risk to the escape route (see Figure 29).

- Protect the escape route with fire-resisting construction to allow people to escape safely past a room in which there is a fire (see Figures 30 and 31).

- Provide an alternative exit (see Figure 32).

Alternative approaches may be acceptable, although expert advice may be necessary.

Fire doors on long corridors should have adequate glazing panels of fire-resistant glass, with the appropriate rating, to allow through vision along the corridor in order to see that the escape way is clear.

Figure 29: Dead-end condition with automatic fire detection (in non-sleeping areas)

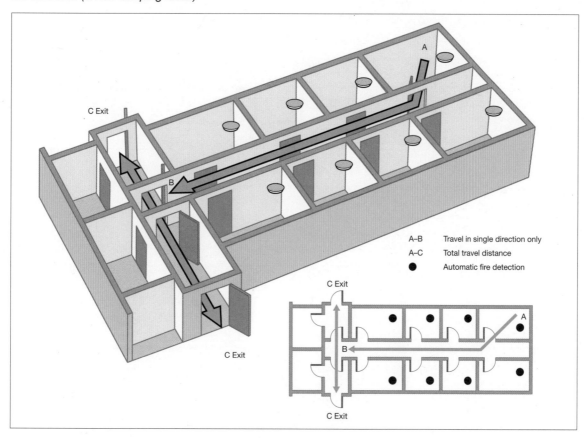

A–B   Travel in single direction only
A–C   Total travel distance
●   Automatic fire detection

Figure 30: Dead-end condition with fire-resisting construction (in non-sleeping areas)

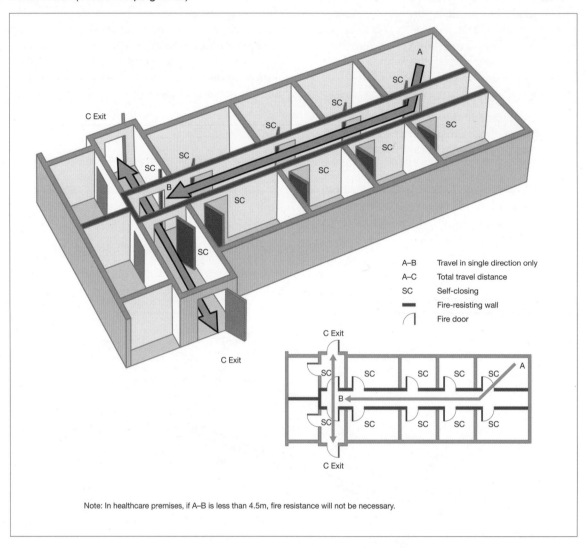

A–B	Travel in single direction only
A–C	Total travel distance
SC	Self-closing
▬	Fire-resisting wall
⌐	Fire door

Note: In healthcare premises, if A–B is less than 4.5m, fire resistance will not be necessary.

Figure 31: Initial dead end with fire-resising construction (e.g. consulting suite in out-patient department, clinic or health centre)

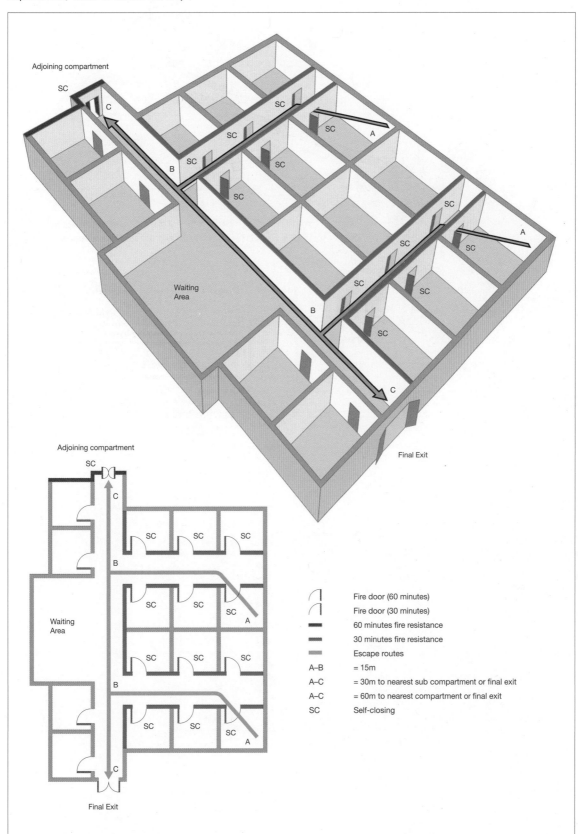

Fire door (60 minutes)
Fire door (30 minutes)
60 minutes fire resistance
30 minutes fire resistance
Escape routes
A–B   = 15m
A–C   = 30m to nearest sub compartment or final exit
A–C   = 60m to nearest compartment or final exit
SC   Self-closing

Figure 32: Dead-end condition provided with an alternative exit

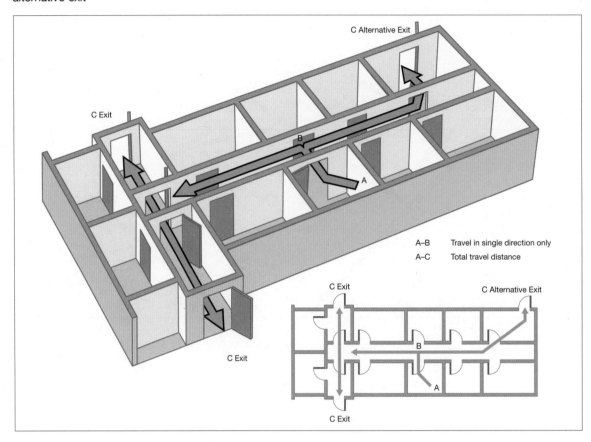

A–B   Travel in single direction only

A–C   Total travel distance

In sleeping areas, the layout shown in Figure 33 will generally be acceptable. However, an alternative approach may be possible if your premises have other supplementary fire protection measures (e.g. an automatic fire suppression system), in which case you should seek expert advice.

Figure 33: Dead end with fire resisting construction and automatic fire detection (in sleeping areas)

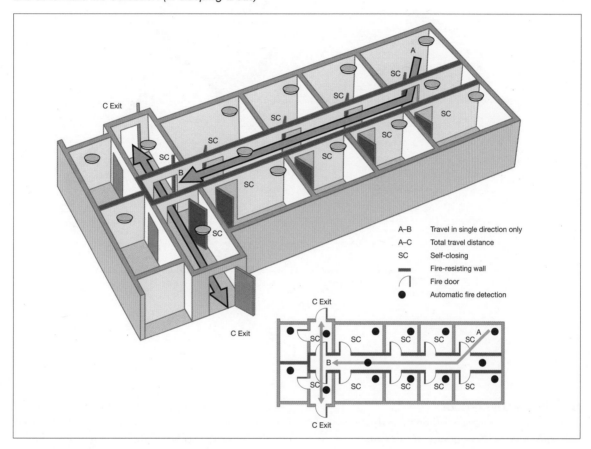

A–B	Travel in single direction only
A–C	Total travel distance
SC	Self-closing
	Fire-resisting wall
	Fire door
●	Automatic fire detection

Basement, escape and protection

In all buildings with basements (other than very small basements), stairways serving upper floors should preferably not extend to the basement, and in any case should not do so when the premises are served by only one stairway. Any stairway that extends from the basement to the upper floors should be separated at basement level by a fire-resisting lobby or corridor between the basement and the stairway.

All basements used by more than 60 members of the public, or where there are no exits directly to a place of safety, should have at least two protected escape stairways.

Where non-ambulant or partially ambulant patients will have access, their means of escape should not necessitate travelling up a stairway to a final exit. Further information can be found in HTM 81.[76]

Wherever possible all stairways to basements should be entered at ground level from the open air, and should be positioned so that smoke from any fire in the basement would not obstruct any exit serving the other floors of the building.

Where any stairway links a basement with the ground floor, the basement should be separated from the ground floor, preferably by two 30-minute fire doors, one at basement and one at ground floor level (see Figure 34).

Any floor over a basement should provide 60 minutes' fire resistance. Where this is impractical, and as long as no smoke can get through the floor, automatic smoke detection linked to a fire-alarm system which is audible throughout the premises could, as an alternative, be provided in the basement area. If in doubt, contact a competent person for more detailed advice.

Figure 34: Basement protection

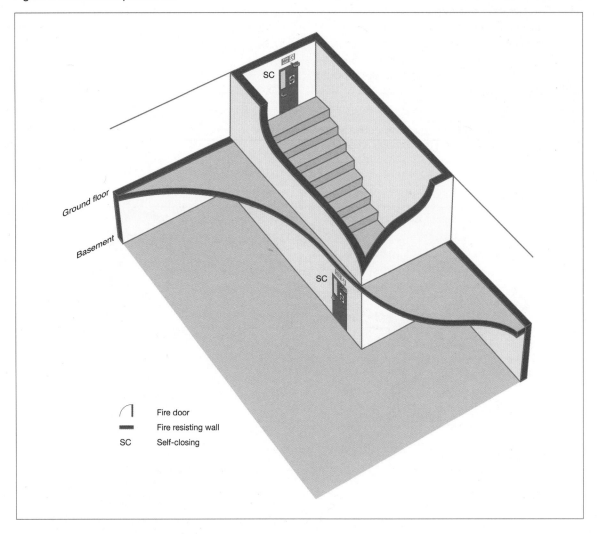

Ground floor

Basement

SC

SC

⌐│ Fire door

▬ Fire resisting wall

SC Self-closing

Subdivision of corridors

In healthcare premises, other than those accommodating dependent or very high dependency patients, where corridors are more than 30m long, then generally these corridors should be subdivided near the centre of the corridor with fire doors and, where necessary, fire-resisting construction to limit the spread of fire and smoke and to protect escape routes if there is a fire. Very often this can be achieved through the use of sub-compartmentation.

In premises where there are dependent or very high dependency patients, Hospital Streets (where used) should be subdivided at 30m intervals. Where other corridors form part of the circulation routes, subdivision with fire doors and fire-resisting construction should be in line with the travel distances for sub-compartmentation. (Note that hospitals without a Hospital Street are designed on the principle of enclosing fire hazard rooms rather than protecting corridors, which would be functionally restrictive.)

Where a corridor serves two exits from a floor, generally these corridors should be subdivided with fire doors to separate the two exits (see Figure 35).

Doors that are provided solely for the purpose of restricting the travel of smoke need not be fire doors, but will be suitable as long as they are of substantial construction, are capable of resisting the passage of smoke, and are self-closing. Doors on circulation routes fitted with a self-closing device should incorporate an electromagnetic hold-open device which is activated by the operation of the fire-detection and alarm system (see Appendix B2). Smoke should not be able to bypass these doors, e.g. above a false ceiling, or via alternative doors from a room, or adjoining rooms, opening on either side of the subdivision.

Generally, false ceilings should be provided with barriers or smoke stopping over any fire doors. Where the false ceiling forms part of the fire-resisting construction this may not be necessary.

In all healthcare premises where a corridor (including a Hospital Street) forms part of the escape route, doors to cupboards, service ducts and any vertical shafts linking floors should be fire doors and identified by notices stating 'Fire door – Keep locked shut when not in use'.

If you have doubts about subdivision of corridors, ask advice from a competent person.

Figure 35: Subdivision of corridor between two stairways or exits

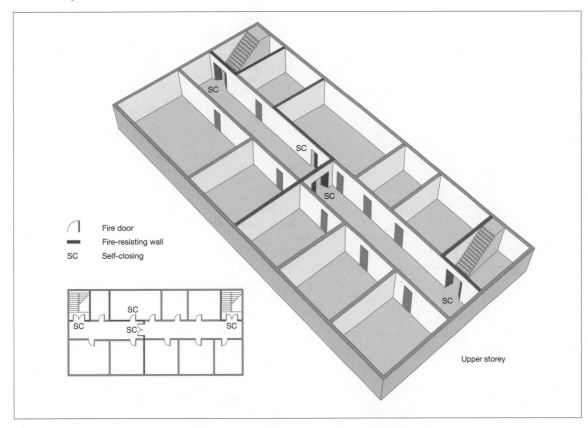

Fire door

Fire-resisting wall

SC Self-closing

Upper storey

Stairway enclosures

Stairways, if unprotected from fire, can rapidly become affected by heat and smoke, cutting off the escape route and allowing fire spread to other floors. However, if adequately protected, escape stairways can be regarded as a place of reasonable safety to enable people to escape to a place of total safety.

In all but the smallest of healthcare premises, there should be a minimum of two stairways. In healthcare premises catering for dependent and very high dependency patients, it is expected that there will be a sufficient number of stairways based on the funtional requirements of the building. Where hospitals are provided with a Hospital Street, stairways can be located within the Hospital Street. In hospitals **not**

provided with a Hospital Street, Firecode indicates that a stairway should be provided to each compartment.

In those premises where only independent patients are likely, stairways used for the emergency evacuation of disabled people should comply with the requirements for internal stairs of the Building Regulations (See Approved Document B)[24]. In healthcare premises where the patients are either dependent or very high dependency, all stairways (other than those within an atrium and only serving the atrium) should be designed as protected stairways. Appropriate dimensions can be found in HTM 81.[76] Specialist evacuation chairs or other equipment may be necessary to negotiaite stairs.

A stairway will be considered suitable if it has direct access, or protected access, to the outside at ground level (see Figure 36). Such access should be suitable for the evacuation of patients and lead to a place of safety away from the building. Alternatively, provide two exits from the stairway, each giving access to a final exit via routes which are separated from each other by fire-resisting construction (see Figure 37).

Figure 36: Example of a protected route from a stairway to a final exit

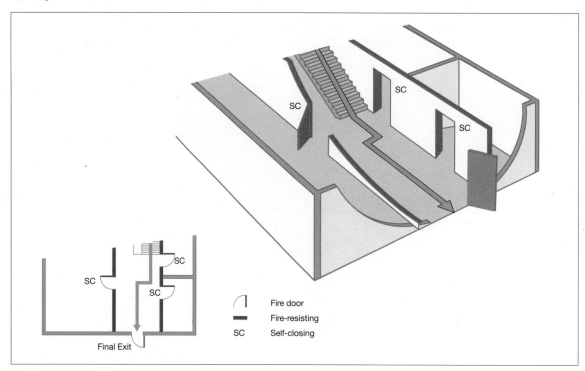

Figure 37: Example of two escape routes from a stairway to final exits

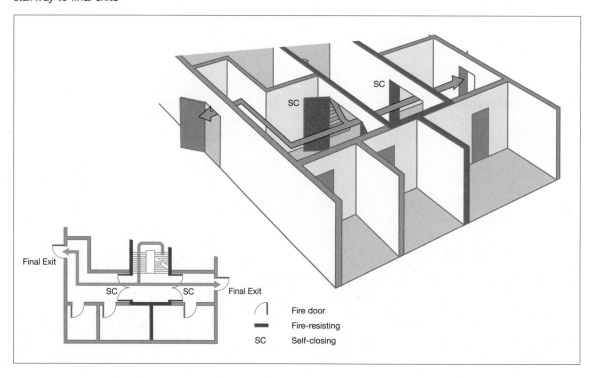

In healthcare premises designed and built to building regulations (HTM 81[76] or HTM 05-02: Part A[76]) and served by more than one stairway, it is probable that most of the stairways will be protected by fire-resisting construction and will lead to a final exit. If any floor has an occupancy of over 60, each storey should have at least two exits, i.e. protected routes. The figure of 60 can be varied in proportion to the risk lower risk slight increase, higher risk: lower numbers of persons.

If you have a protected stairway(s) then it is essential that you maintain that level of fire protection.

The benefit of protecting stairways from the effects of fire is that it allows you to measure your travel distance from the furthest point on the relevant floor to the nearest storey exit rather than the final exit of the building.

It is possible that you may have some stairways which have no fire protection to them. In this case they are not designed for escape and are normally known as accommodation stairways (see page 94, 'Accommodation stairways').

If you do not have a protected stairway (most likely in buildings with independent patients), depending on the outcome of your fire risk assessment it may be that you can achieve an equivalent level of safety by other means. However, before doing so you should seek advice from a competent person.

If the building you occupy is part of a complex with buildings which are occupied by different organisations to your own, you need to consider, as part of your fire risk assessment, the possibility that a fire may occur in another part of the building over which you may have no control and which may affect your protected stairways if allowed to develop unchecked. If your fire risk assessment shows that this may be the case and people using any floor would be unaware of a developing fire, then additional fire-protection measures may be required, e.g. an automatic fire-detection and warning system. If this is required you will need to consult and co-operate with other occupiers and building managers.

You may find that stairways in your building are provided with protected lobbies or corridors at each floor level (except the top floor) (see Figure 38). Although these are not generally necessary for means of escape in multi-stairway buildings of less than 18m high (or five storeys in buildings with dependent and very high dependency patients), they may have been provided for other reasons (e.g. firefighting access). Where lobbies are provided in buildings using progressive horizontal evacuation involving beds or trolleys, it is likely that at some point vertical evacuation using mattresses will be necessary. Therefore, the lobby should be capable of accommodating a mattress. In all cases, lobbies and stairways must be kept clear of combustibles and obstructions.

Figure 38: Examples of a stairway with protected lobby/corridor approach

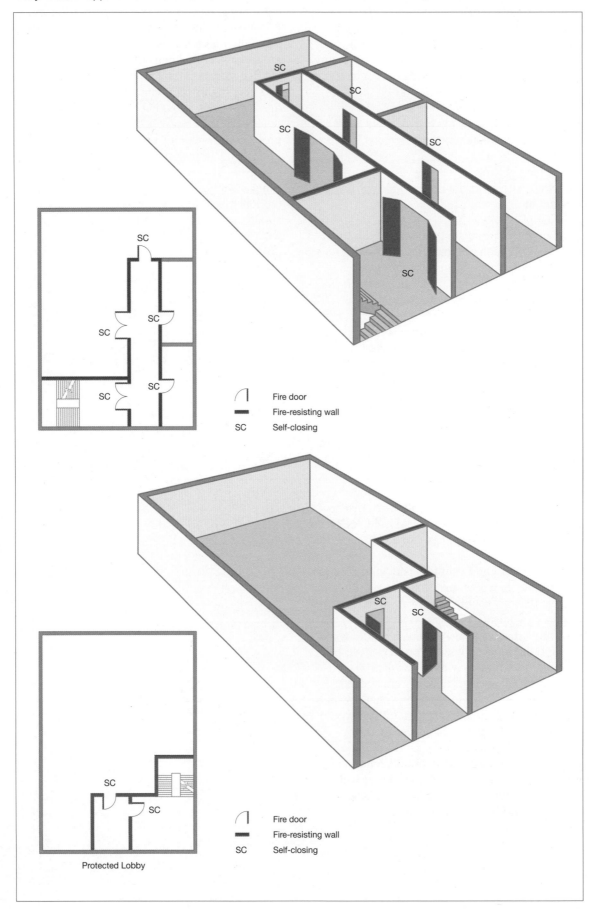

SC   Fire door
▬   Fire-resisting wall
SC   Self-closing

Fire door
Fire-resisting wall
SC   Self-closing

Protected Lobby

Separation of protected stairways

Where there are two or more protected stairways, the routes to final exits should be separated by fire-resisting construction so that fire cannot affect more than one escape route at the same time (see Figure 39).

Figure 39: Separation of protected stairways

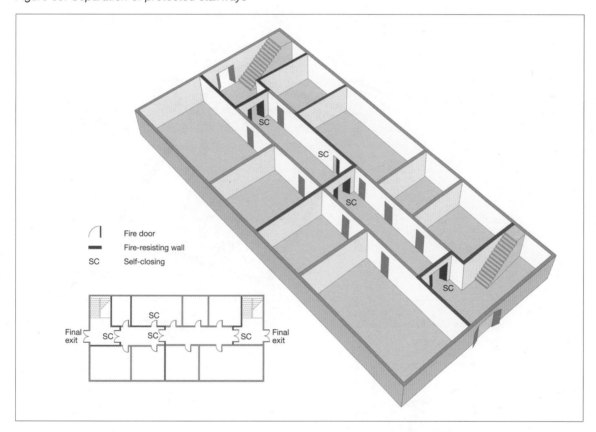

Creating a stairway bypass route

No one should have to pass through a protected stairway to reach another stairway. Options to avoid this include:

- using intercommunicating doors between rooms adjacent to the stairway, such doors must be available at all times when the building is occupied;

- using balconies and other features to bypass the stairway; or

- as long as there is enough space, create a bypass corridor around the stairway enclosure.

An example of one of the above options is illustrated in Figure 40.

Note: If you will be moving patients in beds, trolleys or wheelchairs, you will need to ensure that there is sufficient width throughout the bypass route.

Figure 40: A stairway bypass route

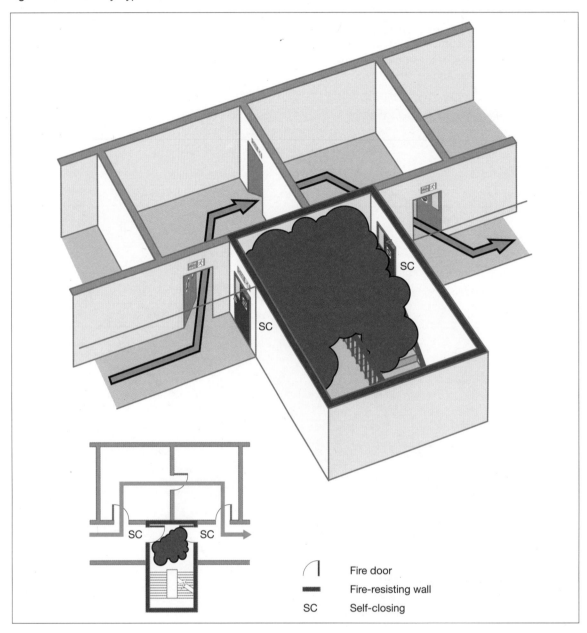

Fire door

Fire-resisting wall

SC   Self-closing

Reception areas

Reception or enquiry areas should only be located in protected stairways where the stairway is not the only one serving the upper floors, the reception area is small (less than 10m²) and is of low fire risk.

Accommodation stairways

If you have stairways that are used for general communication and movement of people in the premises, and they are not designated as escape stairs, then these are called 'accommodation stairways'. They may not require fire separation from the remainder of the floor as long as they do not pass through a fire compartment floor and people do not have to pass the head of such a stairway in order to access a means of escape stairway. However, experience shows that many people will continue to use these as an escape route.

Accommodation stairways should not normally form an integral part of the calculated escape route; however, where your fire risk assessment indicates that it is safe to do so, then you may consider them for that purpose. In these circumstances, it may be necessary to seek advice from a competent person to verify this.

External stairways

To be considered a viable escape route, an external stairway should normally be protected from the effects of a fire along its full length. This means that any door or window (other than toilet windows) and walls within 1.8m horizontally and 9m vertically should be fire-resisting. Windows should be fixed shut and doors self-closing (see Figure 41).

Consider protecting the external stairway from the weather as the treads may become slippery, e.g. due to algae, moss or ice. If this is not possible, you must ensure that the stairway is regularly maintained. Consider fixing non-slip material to the treads.

External stairways are not recommended as a suitable means of escape for dependent or very high dependency patients.

Figure 41: Protection to an external stairway

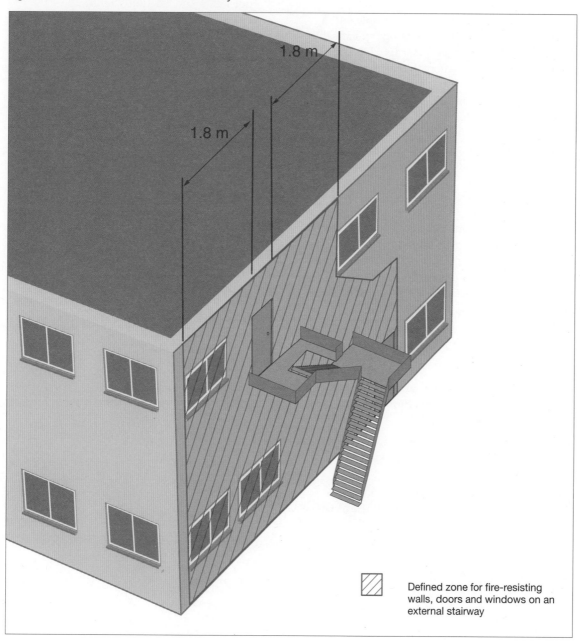

    1.8 m

    1.8 m

Defined zone for fire-resisting walls, doors and windows on an external stairway

Spiral and helical stairways

Existing spiral and helical stairways that are not designed for the purpose should not normally form part of an escape route but, in exceptional situations, may be used by a small number of able bodied staff provided the stairway is not more than 9m in total height, not less than 1.5m in diameter and has adequate headroom and a continuous handrail throughout its full length.

However, spiral and helical stairways that have been designed for the purpose may be used as a means of escape by able bodied staff and by the public but should not be used for the evacuation of patients. Further guidance on type E (public) stairs is given in BS 5395-2.[26]

Lifts

Due to the danger of the power supplies to a lift being affected by a fire, lifts not specifically designed as 'firefighting' or 'escape' lifts are not normally considered acceptable as a means of escape. However, where a lift and stairway for a means of escape are incorporated in a fire-resisting shaft which has a final exit from it at the access level and the lift has a separate electrical supply to that of the remainder of the building, than that lift, subject to an agreed fire risk assessment, may be acceptable as a means of escape in case of fire.

Lifts are housed in vertical shafts that interconnect floors and compartments, therefore precautions have to be taken to protect people from the risk of fire and smoke spreading from floor to floor via the lift shaft. Such precautions may include:

*   separating the lift from the remainder of the storey using fire-resisting construction and access via a fire door;

*   ensuring the lift shaft is situated in a protected enclosure which may also be a stairway enclosure; and

*   providing ventilation of at least 0.1m² at the top of each lift-well to exhaust any smoke.

Additional guidance on escape lifts in healthcare premises can be found in HTM 05-03: Part E.[87]

Roof exits

It may be reasonable for an escape route to cross a roof. Where this is the case, additional precautions will normally be necessary:

*   The roof should be flat and the route across it should be adequately defined and well illuminated where necessary with normal electric and emergency escape lighting.

*   The route should be non-slip and guarded with a protective barrier.

*   The escape route across the roof and its supporting structure should be constructed as a compartment floor.

*   Where there are no alternatives other than to use a roof exit, any doors, windows, roof lights and ducting within 3m of the escape route should be fire-resisting.

*   The exit from the roof should be in, or lead to, a place of reasonable safety where people can quickly move to a place of total safety.

*   Where the escape route passes through or across another person's property, you will need to have a robust legal agreement in place to allow its use at all times when people are on your premises. The agreement should also cover maintenance arrangements for the route.

*   Where practicable, escape routes on flat roofs should be protected from the weather as the surface may become slippery, e.g. due to algae, moss or ice. If this is not possible, you must ensure that the surface is regularly maintained.

A typical escape route across a flat route is illustrated in Figure 42.

Figure 42: An escape route across a roof

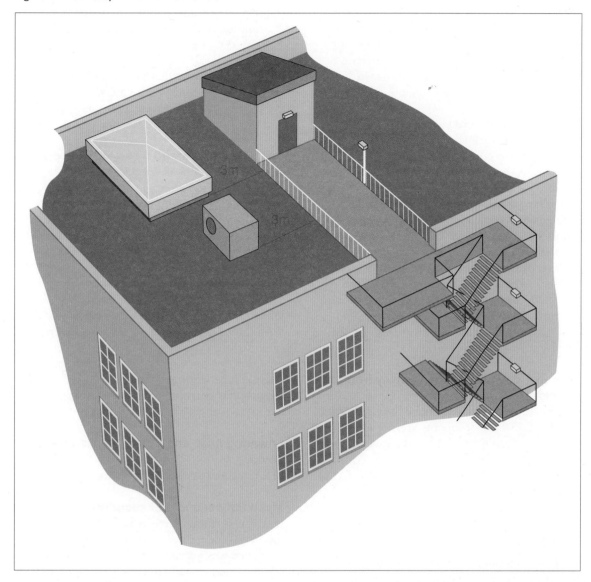

Revolving doors, wicket doors, roller shutters and sliding doors

Revolving doors should be avoided, but where they are used, they must easily convert to outward-opening doors or there must be outward opening doors adjacent to the revolving door, capable of allowing safe egress for the numbers of persons likely to use them. Turnstiles and shutters are not acceptable on escape routes and should not be used.

Sliding doors are acceptable on escape routes in healthcare premises, provided they convert to outward-opening doors when subjected to reasonable pressure from any direction. In the case of powered sliding doors, they should be installed to ensure that they fail safe to the fully open position in the event of a power failure. Where sliding doors are provided, a notice with the words 'Slide to open' and with

an arrow pointing in the appropriate direction should be permanently displayed at about eye-level on the face of the doors.

Wicket doors or gates should not form part of any escape route likely to be used by patients (regardless of their mobility). Where they are installed, wicket doors or gates should have a minimum opening height of 1.5m. The bottom of the door should not be more than 250mm above the floor and the width should be preferably more than 500mm but not less than 450mm. Normally wicket doors will only be suitable for up to 15 members of staff; however, in areas of a higher fire risk, this should be reduced to a maximum of three.

Loading and goods delivery doors, shutters (roller, folding or sliding), up-and-over doors and similar openings are not normally suitable for use on exit routes. However, they may be suitable for escape from areas of normal risk by small numbers of staff as long as they are not likely to be obstructed and can be easily and immediately opened manually (even if normally power-operated) and provided that staff are familiar with their operation.

Wall and floor hatches

Only in exceptional circumstances should it be necessary to rely on wall and floor hatches for means of escape However, there may be some instances when, because of structural difficulties, it will be reasonable to accept arrangements of this kind for a very limited number of persons who are active enough to use them, but under no circumstances should they be provided for the evacuation of patients. Where wall and floor hatches are provided, there may be a need to take special precautions to safeguard against their obstruction and protect their use, e.g. by the provision of guard rails around the hatchway.

Final exit doors and escape away from the premises

Good escape routes to a final exit will be of little benefit if the occupants are not able to get out of the building and move quickly to a place of total safety. It is important to consider where people will go once they have evacuated from the premises.

The matters that you should consider include the following:

- Final exit doors should be quickly and easily openable without a key or code in the event of a fire. Where possible, there should be only one fastening. See Appendix B3 for more information on security fastenings.

- Final exit doors should not lead people into an enclosed area from which there is no further escape.

- Where a final exist discharges into a closed area, further access to a place of total safety should be available by means of gates or doors that open easily in a manner similar to the final exit.

- The route away from the premises needs to be clearly defined, illuminated, signposted, and if necessary protected by guardrails.

- The proximity of other building outlets, such as ventilation and refuse shafts, which may emit smoke and heat from the fire.

- Dangers once away from the building e.g. busy roads and people traffic passing the building, that may affect people on their way out.

Your fire risk assessment must take into account factors such as the mobility of the people who may be expected to use the doors and the accessibility of door opening devices.

Portable ladders and throw-out ladders

Throw-out ladders are not acceptable as a means of escape. Portable ladders are only acceptable in exceptional circumstances where it will be reasonable for ladders of this kind to provide escape for one or two able-bodied staff (e.g. from a high level plant room).

Fixed vertical or raking ladders

These are normally only suitable for use by a limited number of able-bodied staff where they form the only means of access to plant spaces, provided they are suitably guarded and the total descent does not exceed 9m without an intermediate landing. Where they are external they should be protected from the elements in the same way as external stairways.

Lowering lines and other self-rescue devices

These are not acceptable as a means of escape.

Means of escape and security

In most situations there is no conflict between the needs for means of escape and security. However, it is accepted that in certain situations conflicts may arise, particularly in premises which provide accommodation for people with mental illness, where it may be essential to maintain a high level of supervision during an evacuation.

In these situations, doors which open automatically on the activation of the fire alarm system may not be acceptable, since patients would be able to disperse, and not necessarily follow the safest evacuation route, or abscond, possibly placing themselves or others at risk. It would also be more difficult to establish that everyone had been safely removed from the fire-affected area.

In areas where security is important, the staffing levels should be sufficient to allow the operation of a key-operated, or other staff-controlled, evacuation system. Any slight delay in opening doors compared with an automatic system should be compensated for by the ability of a well trained staff team to organise a controlled evacuation more quickly, and with greater confidence, than if the patients had dispersed.

Any solution proposed must be discussed and agreed with the enforcing authorities, healthcare provider and other relevant bodies.

4.2 Escape route layout

The examples listed in Table 3 show typical escape route solutions for a range of healthcare buildings.

These are not intended to be prescriptive or exhaustive but merely to help you understand how the principles of means of escape may be applied in practice.

They are illustrative of the key features of escape route layouts and not intended to be real building layouts or to scale. Further guidance can also be found in HTM 81,[76] HTM 85[79] and Nucleus fire precautions recommendations.

You do not need to read all of this section, you only need to consider those figures and the accompanying text which most closely resemble your premises. If your building does not resemble these then you should seek advice from a competent person. These examples are intended to represent your existing layout; they are not to be used as design guidance.

In all of these examples, the following basic principles apply:

- It is assumed that patients are within the 'independent' or 'dependent' category. Where they fall into the 'very high dependency' category, a higher standard of fire safety provision will be likely.

- The farthest point on any floor to the final exit, storey exit or protected area (compartment or sub-compartment) is within the overall suggested travel distance (see Table 2 on page 78).

- The route to and the area near the exit is kept clear of combustibles and obstructions.

- The protected area or stairway is kept clear of combustibles and obstructions.

- The escape route leads to adjacent compartments and/or a final exit.

- Where the stairway is not a protected stairway, the final exit is visible and accessible from the discharge point of the stairway at ground floor level.

- High-risk rooms do not generally open directly into a protected area or stairway.

- If your fire risk assessment shows that people using any floor would be unaware of a fire you may require additional fire-protection measures, e.g. an automatic fire-detection and warning system.

- There should be more than one escape route from all parts of the premises (rooms or storeys) except for areas or storeys with an occupancy of less than 60. The figure of 60 can be varied in proportion to the risk, for a lower risk there can be a slight increase, for a higher risk, lower numbers of persons should be allowed.

If you do not have any of the configurations given, and depending on the outcome of your fire risk assessment, it may be that you can achieve an equivalent level of safety by other means.

Patient dependency levels have been outlined in Part 1, Step 3.4.3, however, it is necessary to be aware that some patients falling into the 'dependent' category may require additional provisions than would normally be expected. These patients are predominatly:

- unable to walk either with or without assistance; or

- those suffering from mental illness.

Similar additional provisions may be necessary for those areas where very high dependency patients are accommodated.

Additional provisions can include a combination of:

- a high level of observation (greater than 60% of patient beds visible from the staff base); or

- a higher number of staff; or

- a high standard of automatic fire detection and alarm; or

- an automatic fire suppression system; or

- a combination of short travel distances (less than those in Table 2 on page 78) together with a high degree of refuge provision (more than three compartments on the relevent floor) and escape lighting throughout the area, and, on upper floors, the provision of escape lifts.

The above additional provisions are intended to enable first-aid firefighting and increase the time available for escape by way of early detection of the fire, or reduce evacuation time by way of additional staff, or a combination of measures to reduce fire severity due to suppression.

Advice should be sought from a competent person on the suitable additional provisions necessary to mitigate any fire risk to a reasonable level.

Table 3: Typical examples of escape route layouts

Buildings with independent patients	
Single-storey with more than one exit	See Figure 43
Multi-storey with one stairway	See Figure 44
Multi-storey with more than one stairway	See Figure 45
Buildings with dependent or very high dependency patients	
Buildings up to 12m high with a floor area over 1,000m² (without a Hospital Street)	See Figure 46
Buildings up to 12m high with a floor area over 1,000m² (with a Hospital Street)	See Figure 47
Buildings over 12m high with a floor area over 1,000m² (without a Hospital Street)	See Figure 48
Buildings over 12m high with a floor area over 1,000m² (with a Hospital Street)	See Figure 49
Typical Nucleus template layout	See Figure 50
Typical arrangement for Nucleus fire compartments	See Figure 51

Buildings with independent patients

Single-storey with more than one exit

Figure 43 shows a single-storey building
with more than one exit, which might be
representative of GP premises, a walk-in
centre, a clinic or health centre. Travel
distances should be in line with Table 2
on page 78 for independent patients.

*Figure 43: Single storey premises with more than
one exit*

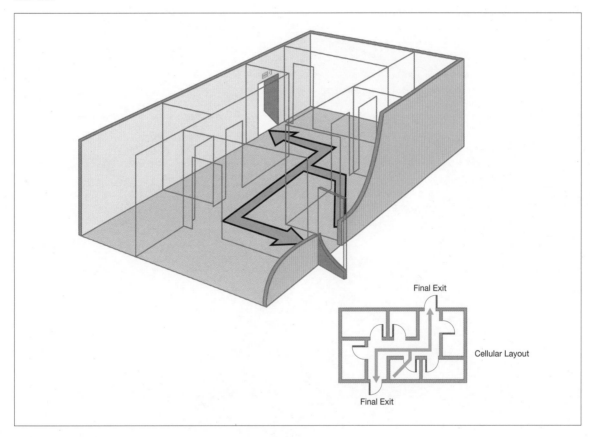

Final Exit

Cellular Layout

Final Exit

Multi-storey with one stairway

In healthcare premises a single stairway may be acceptable in some smaller multi-storey buildings used by independent patients (e.g. a health centre or GP surgery). The layout shown in Figure 44 will generally be acceptable as long as the following apply:

• The upper floors or any basement should individually accommodate no more than 60 people.

• The furthest point on each floor to the storey exit is with the overall suggested travel distance for a single escape route (independent patients).

• The floor level of the highest storey is not more than 11m above the ground.

Figure 44: Multi-storey with one stairway

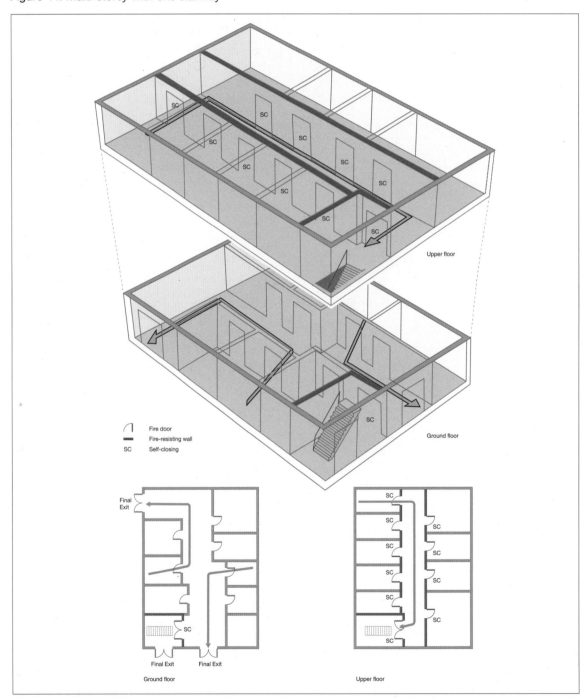

Multi-storey with more than one stairway

In multi-storey healthcare buildings used by independent patients (e.g. a health centre or GP surgery) the layout shown in Figure 45 will generally be acceptable.

Note: The principles shown apply to all buildings which have no storey with any floor more than 18m above the ground. However, if your building has more than three floors above ground you should seek the advice of a competent person.

Figure 45: Multi-storey with more than one stairway

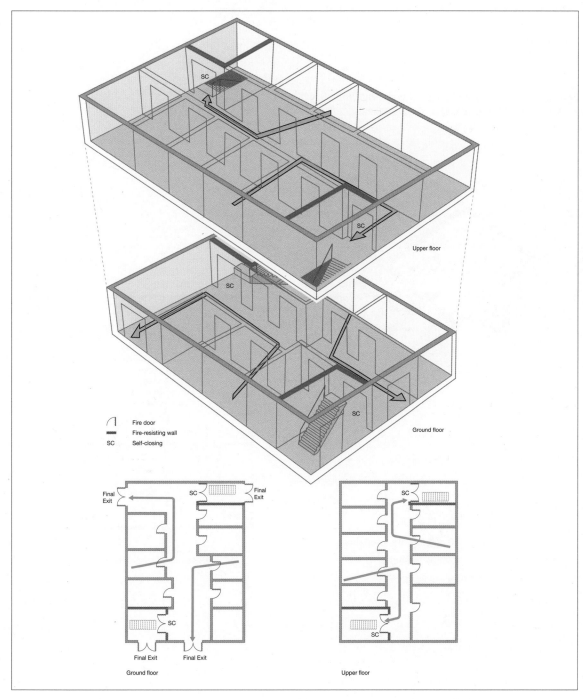

Buildings with dependent or very high dependency patients

Buildings up to 12m high with a floor area over 1,000m² (without a Hospital Street)

Figure 46 shows the typical design layout for a healthcare building with dependent and very high dependency patients requiring at least three compartments. There should be a minimum of three exits from each compartment, two of which lead to adjoining but separate compartments, the other to a stairway or final exit.

Figure 46: Buildings up to 12m high with a floor area over 1,000m² (without a Hospital Street)

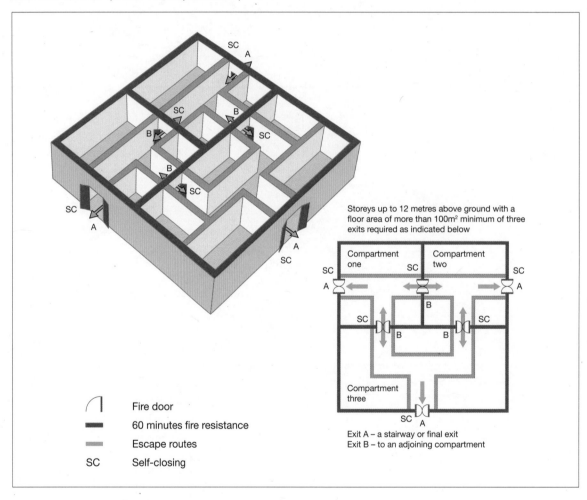

Storeys up to 12 metres above ground with a floor area of more than 100m² minimum of three exits required as indicated below

Compartment one
Compartment two
Compartment three

Exit A – a stairway or final exit
Exit B – to an adjoining compartment

Symbol	Description
Fire door	
60 minutes fire resistance	
Escape routes	
SC	Self-closing

Buildings up to 12m high with a floor area over 1,000m² (with a Hospital Street)

Figure 47 shows the typical design layout for a healthcare building with dependent and very high dependency patients requiring at least three compartments, one of which may be a Hospital Street. There should be a minimum of two exits from each compartment, one to an adjoining compartment and the other to the Hospital Street.

Figure 47: Buildings up to 12m high with a floor area over 1000m² (with a Hospital Street)

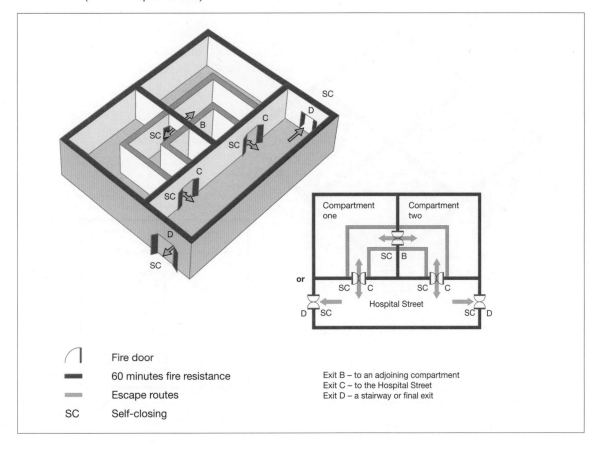

Fire door

60 minutes fire resistance

Escape routes

SC Self-closing

Exit B – to an adjoining compartment
Exit C – to the Hospital Street
Exit D – a stairway or final exit

Buildings over 12m high with a floor area over 1,000m² (without a Hospital Street)

Figure 48 shows the typical design layout for a healthcare building with dependent and very high dependency patients requiring at least four compartments. There should be a minimum of three exits from each compartment, two of which lead to adjoining but separate compartments, the third to a stairway or final exit.

Figure 48: Buildings over 12m high with a floor area over 1,000m² (without a Hospital Street)

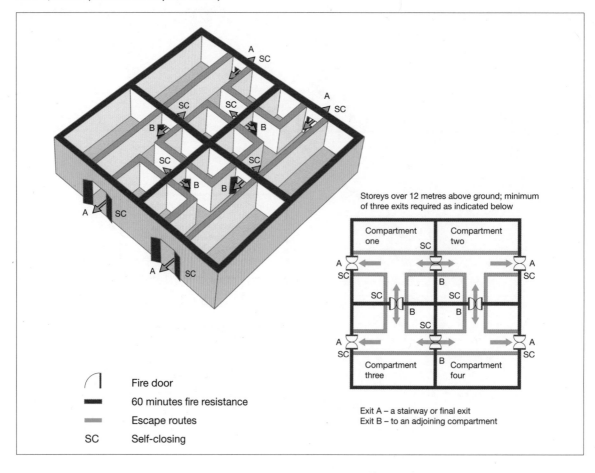

Storeys over 12 metres above ground; minimum of three exits required as indicated below

Compartment one	Compartment two

Exit A – a stairway or final exit
Exit B – to an adjoining compartment

Fire door

60 minutes fire resistance

Escape routes

SC   Self-closing

Buildings over 12m high with a floor area over 1,000m² (with a Hospital Street)

Figure 49 shows the typical design layout for a healthcare building with dependent and very high dependency patients requiring at least four compartments, one of which may be a Hospital Street. There should be a minimum of two exits from each compartment, one to an adjoining compartment and the other to the Hospital Street.

Figure 49: Buildings over 12m high with a floor area over 1,000m² (with a Hospital Street)

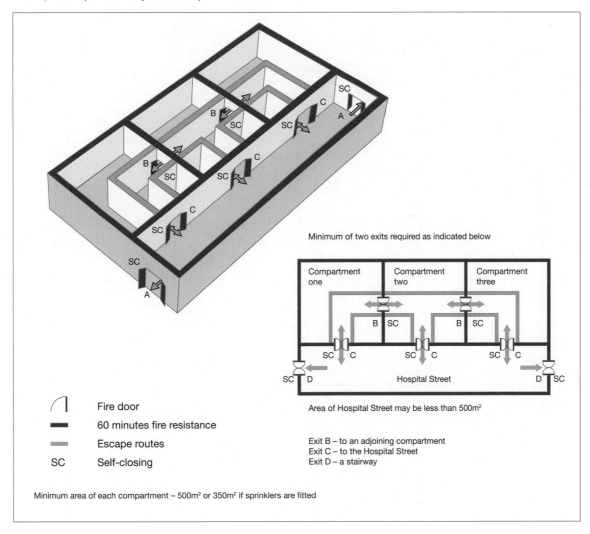

Minimum of two exits required as indicated below

Area of Hospital Street may be less than 500m²

Fire door
60 minutes fire resistance
Escape routes
SC   Self-closing

Exit B – to an adjoining compartment
Exit C – to the Hospital Street
Exit D – a stairway

Minimum area of each compartment – 500m² or 350m² if sprinklers are fitted

Typical Nucleus template layout

Figure 50 shows the typical layout of a Nucleus hospital template and the intended escape routes from a standard Nucleus template. Further information relating to Nucleus hospitals can be found at Appendix E.

Figure 50: Typical Nucleus template layout

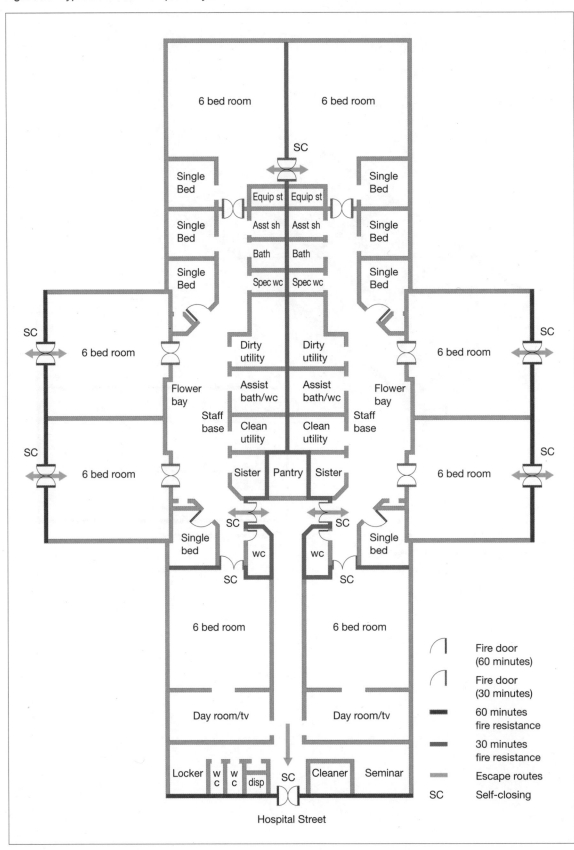

Typical arrangement for Nucleus fire compartments

Figure 51 shows the typical arrangement for interconnecting Nucleus hospital templates.

Figure 51: Typical arrangement for Nucleus fire compartments

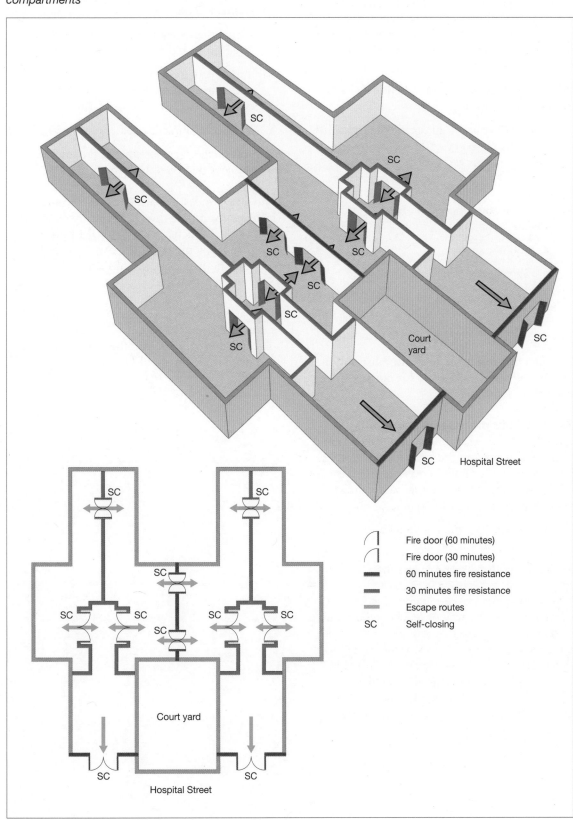

Fire door (60 minutes)
Fire door (30 minutes)
60 minutes fire resistance
30 minutes fire resistance
Escape routes
SC   Self-closing

Additional precautions for certain healthcare premises

Ground to second-floor premises with poor observation of patients' beds

Many fires are detected by staff on the ward observing smoke at the early stage of development of a fire. To improve patient experience and privacy means that many wards have single bedrooms, which generally means that fewer patient beds are observable from the staff base.

Where observation is poor, additional protection can include:

- a high standard of automatic fire detection in all sleeping areas, fire hazard rooms and circulation spaces;

- a higher number of staff;

- an automatic suppression system, such as a water sprinkler system; or

- a combination of:

  - Short travel distances; and

  - A high degree of refuge areas, i.e. the number of protected areas on the same level is greater than three.

It is also possible to increase the observation, but this may be undesirable for nursing or clinical reasons.

Second-floor premises with no refuge

If a patient care area is situated on the second floor of a healthcare premises for which there is no potential for refuge, because there is only one compartment or sub-compartment, additional protection can include:

- relocating the patient care area to the ground or first floor; and

- ensuring that its area is less than 900m².

The above measures are intended to reduce evacuation time by way of reducing the number of stairs to be negotiated and the number of patients to be evacuated. However, in many practical situations it will be more desirable from a functional and cost perspective to increase the level of refuge by either compartmentation or sub-compartmentation.

Third-floor patient care area

The greater the height at which patients are located, the more difficult it is for them to receive assistance in the event of a fire or use vertical evacuation should that become necessary. Therefore, the additional protection for patients on a third-storey area can include a combination of:

- a high degree of refuge, i.e. more than three protected areas on the same level;

- a high provision of stairways, i.e. at least one stairway provided in every compartment (where there is no Hospital Street);

- small compartments, i.e. less than 900m²; and

- access and facilities for the fire and rescue services that comply with HTM 81.[76]

The above measures are intended to enhance facilities for progressive horizontal evacuation and vertical evacuation should that become necessary. Alternatively, it may be possible to relocate the patient accommodation at some time in the future.

For patient care areas higher than the third storey, a bespoke solution will either be in place or be required, and the advice of a competent person should be sought.

Section 5 Further guidance on emergency escape lighting

The primary purpose of emergency escape lighting is to illuminate escape routes but it also illuminates other safety equipment.

The size and type of your premises and the risk to the occupants will determine the complexity of emergency escape lighting required.

Single 'stand-alone' emergency escape lighting units may be sufficient in smaller premises and these can sometimes be combined with exit or directional signs. The level of general illumination should not be significantly reduced by the sign.

For most healthcare premises, a more comprehensive system of fixed automatic emergency escape lighting is likely to be needed. This will be particularly true in premises with extensive basements or where there are significant numbers of staff or members of the public. In these circumstances, emergency escape lighting is required to light circulation spaces and escape routes in the event of a fire or to guard against a failure of electrical supply. HTM 2011[89] ('Emergency electrical services') and HTM 2007[88] ('Electrical services supply and distribution') give guidance on emergency escape lighting and details of the electrical supply required for large healthcare premises such as hospitals.

You will have identified the escape routes when carrying out your fire risk assessment and need to ensure that they are all adequately lit. If there are escape routes that are not permanently illuminated by normal lighting, such as external stairs, then a switch, clearly marked 'Escape lighting', or some other means of switching on the lighting should be provided at the entry to that area/stairs.

An emergency escape lighting system should normally cover the following:

- each exit door;

- escape routes;

- intersections of corridors;

- outside each final exit and on external escape routes;

- emergency escape signs;

- stairways so that each flight receives adequate light;

- changes in floor level;

- windowless rooms and toilet accommodation exceeding 8m²;

- firefighting equipment;

- fire alarm call points;

- equipment that would need to be shut down in an emergency;

- lifts; and

- areas greater than 60m².

It is not necessary to provide individual lights (luminaires) for each item above, but there should be a sufficient overall level of light to allow them to be visible and usable.

Emergency escape lighting can be both 'maintained', i.e. on all the time, or 'non-maintained', which only operates when the normal lighting fails. Systems or individual luminaires are designed to operate for durations of between one and three hours. In practice, the three-hour design is the most popular and can help with maintaining limited continued use of your premises during a power failure (other than in an emergency situation).

Figure 52: Luminaires

Emergency escape lighting (luminaires) can be stand-alone dedicated units or incorporated into normal light fittings. There are highly decorative versions of these for those areas that demand aesthetically pleasing fixtures. Power supplies can be rechargeable batteries integral to each unit, a central battery bank or an automatic start generator.

To complement emergency escape lighting, you may wish to identify exit routes by the use of way-guidance equipment. Way-guidance systems usually comprise photo-luminescent material, lines of LEDs, or strips of miniature incandescent lamps, forming a continuous marked escape route at lower level (see Figure 53). These systems have proved particularly effective when people have to escape through smoke, and for partially-sighted people. They can be particularly useful in premises providing healthcare where they can provide marked routes on floors and can direct people to escape routes which are seldom used.

If you decide that you need to install emergency escape lighting or to modify your existing system, any work should be carried out by a competent person in accordance with the appropriate standards.

Further guidance is given in BS 5266-1[28] and BS 5266-8.[27]

Figure 53: A 'way-guidance' system

Maintenance and testing of emergency escape lighting

All emergency escape lighting systems should be regularly tested and properly maintained to an appropriate standard. Most existing systems will need to be manually tested. However,

some modern systems have self-testing facilities that reduce routine checks to a minimum.

Depending on your type of installation you should be able to carry out most of the routine tests yourself. The test method will vary. If you are not sure how to carry out these tests you should contact your supplier or other competent person.

Figure 54: A test key

Test facilities often take the form of a 'fishtail' key inserted in a special switch (see Figure 54), either near the main fuse board or adjacent to relevant light switches.

Typically, testing would include:

- a daily visual check of any central controls;

- a monthly function test by operating the test facility for a period sufficient to ensure that each emergency lamp illuminates; and

- an annual full discharge test.

Particular care needs to be taken following a full discharge test. Batteries typically take 24 hours to re-charge and the premises should not be re-occupied until the emergency lighting system is fully functioning unless alternative arrangements have been made. It is good practice to keep a record of such tests.

In hospitals, this is unlikely to apply as they are occupied 24 hours a day, seven days a week, and most emergency lighting is provided on the essential power supply. Otherwise, systems should be tested on a zonal basis as appropriate and alternative management arrangements, potentially including the use of torches, may be used in the event of an emergency.

Further guidance on maintenance of emergency escape lighting is given in BS 5266-8.[27]

Section 6 Further guidance on signs and notices

Escape signs

In small and simple premises, a few signs indicating the alternative exit(s) might be all that is needed. In larger and more complex premises, a series of signs directing people along the escape routes towards the final exit might be needed.

Many people with poor vision retain some sight and are able to recognise changing or contrasting colour to provide them with visual clues when moving around a building.* It may be sufficient to paint any columns and walls in a contrasting colour and to highlight changes in level by, for example, making the nosing to step and stair treads a contrasting colour (see BS 8300[14]).

For people with no sight, a well-managed 'buddy system', continuous handrails or a sound localisation system (which helps people to move towards an alert sound), or the installation of more tactile aids may be appropriate.

Exit signs should be clearly visible whenever the public, staff and contractors are present in the building.

Positioning of escape signs

The presence of other signs in premises (such as notices and patients' information) or decorations can distract attention from, or obscure the visibility of, escape signs. This could affect people's ability to see and understand escape signs, particularly if there is a fire evacuation. Always ensure that escape signs are not overwhelmed.

Escape signs should meet the following criteria:

- They should provide clear, unambiguous information to enable people to safely leave a building in an emergency.

- Every escape route sign should, where necessary, incorporate, or be accompanied by, a directional arrow. Arrows should not be used on their own.

- If the escape route to the nearest exit is not obvious then it should be indicated by a sign(s).

- Signs should be positioned so that a person escaping will always have the next escape route sign in sight.

- Escape signs should be fixed above the door in the direction of escape and not be fixed to doors, as they will not be visible if the door is open.

- Signs mounted above doors should be at a height of between 2.0m and 2.5m above the floor.

- Signs on walls should be mounted between 1.7m and 2.0m above the floor.

- Mounting heights greater than 2.5m may be used for hanging signs, e.g. in large open spaces or for operational reasons, but care should be taken to ensure that such signs are both conspicuous and legible. In such case larger signs may be necessary.

- Signs should be sited at the same height throughout the escape route, so far as is reasonably practicable.

Escape sign design

For a sign to comply with the signs and signals regulations it must be in pictogram form (see Figures 55 and 56). The pictogram can be supplemented by text if this is considered necessary to make the sign easily understood (BS-type sign), but you must not have a safety sign that uses only text. Either type of sign will be acceptable but different types should not be mixed. Appropriate signs should take into account the needs of those who may need to use them.

The legibility of escape signs is determined by the size of the sign, its level of illumination and the distance over which it is viewed. The use of signs within the same premises should follow a consistent design pattern or scheme. You should not rely on a few outsized signs which may encourage people to travel to a particular escape route when other more appropriate routes should be used.

In multi-occupied premises, co-ordination between the respective 'responsible persons' should be sought to ensure that, as far as possible, all signs in the building conform to a single pattern or scheme.

* The Royal National Institute of the Blind estimates that only about 4% of visually impaired people are totally blind.

Figure 55: BS-type sign

Figure 56: Euro sign

Other safety signs and notices

A number of other mandatory signs such as 'Fire action' notices may also be necessary.

Fire doors that have been fitted with self-closing devices should be labelled 'Fire door – keep shut' (Figure 57) on both sides. Fire-resisting doors to cupboards, stores and service ducts that are not self-closing because they are routinely kept locked should be labelled 'Fire door – keep locked' on the outside.

Figure 57: 'Fire door keep shut' notice

Signs should indicate non-automatic fire safety equipment if there is any doubt about its location, e.g. fire extinguishers that are kept in cabinets or in recesses.

A notice with the words 'Push bar to open' should be permanently displayed immediately above the push-bar on all doors fitted with a panic bolt or panic latch.

A notice with the words 'Fire escape – keep clear' should be permanently displayed at about eye level on the external face of all doors which are provided solely as a means of escape in case of fire and which, because they are not normally used, may become obstructed.

Staff notices

In simple premises providing healthcare where there is a limited number of escape routes, it may be reasonable to provide staff with verbal reminders of what they need to do if there is a fire. In some premises, you could consider providing this in a short written statement that could, for example, be delivered with staff pay slips every six months.

In larger and more complex premises or where there is a high turnover of staff, a more considered approach for staff notices and instructions will be necessary. As well as positioning the fire instructions notice on escape routes adjacent to fire break-glass call points (Figure 58), put them where staff frequently assemble in the premises, e.g. the staff room and locker rooms. Further guidance on appropriate notices can be found in HTM 83.[78]

Figure 58: A typical staff action notice

If your premises are routinely expected to accommodate large numbers of people whose first language is not English, you may need to consider providing instruction in more than one language. The interpretation should always convey an identical message.

Illumination

All signs and notices will need illumination to ensure they are conspicuous and legible. There are a number of options available to achieve this, such as:

- external illumination; and

- internal illumination.

The supplier or other competent person can give you further advice.

Signs or notices of the photo-luminescent type, i.e. where the active material making up the luminous parts of such signs or notices needs a period of exposure to light before they become visible in darkness (but get fainter with time), are not a substitute for appropriate emergency lighting and should only be used where other forms of illumination are present.

Further guidance

Detailed guidance on fire safety signs can be found in BS 5499-4[29] and BS 5499-5.[69] Published guidance[5,6] on compliance with health and safety legislation on signs is also available. Guidance about photo-luminescent fire safety signs and notices can be found in BS 5266-6.[68]

Section 7 Further guidance on recording, planning, informing, instructing and training

7.1 Fire safety records

Keeping up-to-date records of your fire risk assessment can help you effectively manage the fire strategy for your premises and demonstrate how you are complying with fire safety law.

Even if you do not have to record the fire risk assessment, it can be helpful to keep a record of any co-operation and exchange of information made between employers and other responsible people for future reference.

In larger and more complex premises, it is best to keep a dedicated record of all maintenance of fire-protection equipment and training. There is no one 'correct' format specified for this. Suitable record books are available from trade associations and may also be available from your local enforcing authority.

In all cases the quality of records may also be regarded as a good indicator of the overall quality of the safety management structure.

Your records should be kept in a specified place on the premises (for example, in the management's office), and should include:

- details of any significant findings from the fire risk assessment and any action taken (see Part 1, Section 4.1);

- testing and checking of escape routes, including final exit locking mechanisms, such as panic devices, emergency exit devices and any electromagnetic devices;

- testing of fire-warning systems, including weekly alarm tests and periodic maintenance by a competent person;

- recording of false alarms;

- testing and maintenance of emergency escape lighting systems;

- testing and maintenance of fire extinguishers, hose reels and fire blankets, etc;

- if appropriate, testing and maintenance of other fire safety equipment such as fire-suppression systems and smoke control systems;

- recording and training of relevant people and fire evacuation drills;

- planning, organising, policy and implementation, monitoring, audit and review;

- maintenance and audit of any systems that are provided to help the fire and rescue service;

- the arrangements in a multi-occupied building for a co-ordinated emergency plan or overall control of the actions you or your staff should take if there is a fire; and

- all alterations, tests, repairs and maintenance of fire safety systems, including passive systems such as fire doors.

Other issues that you may wish to record include:

- the competence, qualifications and status of the persons responsible for carrying out inspections and tests;

- the results of periodic safety audits, reviews, inspections and tests, and any remedial action taken;

- all incidents and circumstances which had the potential to cause accidents and monitor subsequent remedial actions; and

- a record of the building use, the fire prevention and protection measures in place and high-risk areas.

You should ensure that no other management decisions or policies compromise safety.

In premises with 'engineered fire safety strategies', a fire policy manual should be provided in addition to any other records. Guidance on the structure of fire engineering policy manuals is given in BS 7974-0 section 5: Reporting and presentation.[30]

Your documentation should be available for inspection by representatives of the enforcing authority.

More detailed advice is given in BS 5588-12.[58]

Figures 59–62 give examples of how to record significant findings of your risk assessment, with regard to the type of patient dependency. A blank version of this form is provided in Appendix A2.

Figure 59: Example record of significant findings – independent patient occupancy

Risk Assessment – Record of significant findings

Risk assessment for		Assessment undertaken by	
Company	Anytown Health Centre	Date	25/05/2006
Address	Anytown	Completed by	A B Smith
		Signature	A B Smith

Floor level	Use
Ground	Health Centre

Step 1 – Identify fire hazards

Sources of ignition	Sources of fuel	Sources of oxygen
• Electric heaters, toaster, microwave, kettle, open flame sterilising equipment	• Alcohol, textiles, furniture, disposable products, stationary, domestic & clinical waste	• Medical oxygen cyclinder

Step 2 – People at risk

• 14 full-time and 6 part-time staff, 1 disabled staff (hearing impairment), 30 patients (peak period)

Step 3 – Evaluate, remove, reduce and protect from risk

(3.1) Evaluate the risk of the fire occuring	• Flammable materials adjacent to open flame-producing equipment. Toaster too close to cupboards.
(3.2) Evaluate the risk to people from a fire starting in the premises	• Open plan area with good visibility – fire quickly evident. Escape routes have no fire detection. Waste stored on escape routes.
(3.3) Remove and reduce the hazards that may cause a fire	• Use a safer alternative to open flame equipment. Re-position toaster. Move waste to a dedicated store.
(3.4) Remove and reduce the risks to people from a fire	Current fire precautions are indicated on attached plan and have been assessed as part of the risk assessment. They will be considered adequate with the following additions: • provide automatic fire detection to escape routes. • replace door to waste store with half-hour fire-resisting door and keep locked shut.

Assessment review

Assessment review date	Completed by	Signature

Review outcome (where substantial changes have occurred a new record sheet should be used)

Notes:

(1) The risk assessment record of significant findings should refer to other plans, records or other documents as necessary.

(2) The information in this record should assist you to develop an emergency plan; coordinate measures with other 'responsible persons' in the building; and to inform and train staff and inform other relevant persons.

Figure 60: Example record of significant findings – dependent patient occupancy

Risk Assessment – Record of significant findings

Risk assessment for		Assessment undertaken by	
Building	K Block Anytown Hospital	Date	25/05/2006
		Completed by	A B Smith
Location	Ward 3	Signature	A B Smith

Floor level	Use
2nd	Orthopaedic Ward

Step 1 – Identify fire hazards

Sources of ignition	Sources of fuel	Sources of oxygen
• Microwave, toaster, hot water boiler, 2 ring electric hob, smoking, deliberate ignition	• Textiles and furniture, disposable products, dressings, domestic and clinical waste, medical gases Sources of oxygen	• Medical oxygen in cylinders

Step 2 – People at risk

• 8 full-time and 4 part-time staff at any one time, 6 peripatetic staff, 28 patients, 90 visitors (peak time)

Step 3 – Evaluate, remove, reduce and protect from risk

(3.1) Evaluate the risk of the fire occuring
• Flammable materials adjacent to microwave/hot water boiler. Toaster too close to cupboards. Smoking policy not adhered to

(3.2) Evaluate the risk to people from a fire starting in the premises
• More than 50% of patients are not ambulant. Observation is poor due to ward design (4 and 6-bed rooms)

(3.3) Remove and reduce the hazards that may cause a fire
• Re-position the toaster (taking account of smoke detector positions). Re-enforce smoking policy. Remove flammable materials

(3.4) Remove and reduce the risks to people from a fire
• An L1 fire-detection and alarm system is already installed throughout the ward
• The existing fire precautions are identified on fire plans available on the ward
• The ward has been assessed using HTM 86 Fire risk assessment in hospitals. Subject to the matters identified above, the precautions are considered to be adequate

Assessment review

Assessment review date	Completed by	Signature

Review outcome (where substantial changes have occurred a new record sheet should be used)

Notes:
(1) The risk assessment record of significant findings should refer to other plans, records or other documents as necessary.
(2) The information in this record should assist you to develop an emergency plan; coordinate measures with other 'responsible persons' in the building; and to inform and train staff and inform other relevant persons.

Figure 61: Example record of significant findings – very high dependency patient occupancy

Risk Assessment – Record of significant findings

Risk assessment for		Assessment undertaken by	
Building	L Block Anytown Hospital	Date	25/05/2006
		Completed by	A B Smith
Location	ICU	Signature	A B Smith

Floor level	Use
4th Floor	Intensive Care Unit

Step 1 – Identify fire hazards

Sources of ignition	Sources of fuel	Sources of oxygen
• Large quantity of electrical medical equipment, toaster, microwave.	• Textiles and furniture, disposable products, dressings, domestic and clinical waste, medical gases	• Medical oxygen in cylinders and piped supply.

Step 2 – People at risk

• 6 full-time and 4 part time staff present at any time, 4 peripatetic staff, 6 patients and 18 visitors (peak time)

Step 3 – Evaluate, remove, reduce and protect from risk

(3.1) Evaluate the risk of the fire occuring	• Large quantity of electrical medical equipment, which is regularly tested and maintained. Toaster too close to cupboards.
(3.2) Evaluate the risk to people from a fire starting in the premises	• No patients would be able to evacuate without assistance. It would take a minimum of 15 minutes to prepare each patient for evacuation.
(3.3) Remove and reduce the hazards that may cause a fire	• The toaster should be re-positioned (taking account of smoke detector positions). It is not possible to remove any of the electrical equipment.
(3.4) Remove and reduce the risks to people from a fire	• This ward has been assessed using HTM 86 Fire risk assessment in hospitals. It is not possible to further reduce the risks to people from fire in this location. However, there is a high standard of fire detection and alarm provision. There is also a high ratio of staff to patients. Travel distances are shorter than those set out in Firecode. These additional factors meet the very high standards set out in HTM 86. • Given these very high standards, these factors are considered to be adequate subject to the re-positioning of the toaster.

Assessment review

Assessment review date	Completed by	Signature

Review outcome (where substantial changes have occurred a new record sheet should be used)

Notes:

(1) The risk assessment record of significant findings should refer to other plans, records or other documents as necessary.

(2) The information in this record should assist you to develop an emergency plan; coordinate measures with other 'responsible persons' in the building; and to inform and train staff and inform other relevant persons.

Figure 62: Example record of significant findings – Nucleus hospital design

Risk Assessment – Record of significant findings

Risk assessment for		Assessment undertaken by	
Building	Wilson Unit Benefit Hospital	Date	25/05/2006
		Completed by	A B Smith
Location	Ward 27	Signature	A B Smith

Floor level	Use
1st	Adult acute ward

Step 1 – Identify fire hazards

Sources of ignition	Sources of fuel	Sources of oxygen
• Microwave, toaster, hot water boiler, 2 ring electric hob, smoking, deliberate ignition.	• Textiles and furniture, disposable products, dressings, domestic and clinical waste, medical gases.	• Medical oxygen in cylinders and piped supply.

Step 2 – People at risk

• 8 full-time and 4 part-time staff at any time, 4 peripatetic staff, 28 patients, 56 patients at peak times

Step 3 – Evaluate, remove, reduce and protect from risk

(3.1) Evaluate the risk of the fire occuring	• Toaster too close to cupboards. Smoking policy not adhered to. No policy on arson.
(3.2) Evaluate the risk to people from a fire starting in the premises	• Up to 30% of patients are not ambulant. There is limited observation from the staff base due to ward design (6 bed rooms).
(3.3) Remove and reduce the hazards that may cause a fire	• Re-position the toaster (taking account of smoke detector positions). Re-enforce smoking policy. Write a policy on arson.
(3.4) Remove and reduce the risks to people from a fire	• The fire detection and alarm system installed is in accordance with the guidance in Nucleus fire precautions recommendations. • The existing fire precautions are identified on fire plans available on the ward. • The ward has been assessed using Nucleus fire risk assessment. Subject to the matters identified above, the precautions are considered to be adequate.

Assessment review

Assessment review date	Completed by	Signature

Review outcome (where substantial changes have occurred a new record sheet should be used)

Notes:

(1) The risk assessment record of significant findings should refer to other plans, records or other documents as necessary.

(2) The information in this record should assist you to develop an emergency plan; coordinate measures with other 'responsible persons' in the building; and to inform and train staff and inform other relevant persons.

Fire safety audit

A fire safety audit can be used alongside your fire risk assessment to identify what fire safety provisions exist in your premises.

When carrying out a review of your fire safety risk assessment, a pre-planned audit can quickly identify if there have been any significant changes which may affect the fire safety systems and highlight whether there is a need to revise the fire risk assessment.

Plans and specifications

Plans and specifications can be required to assist understanding of a fire risk assessment or emergency plan. Even where not needed for this purpose they can help you and your staff keep your fire risk assessment and emergency plan under review and help the fire and rescue service in the event of fire. Any symbols used should be shown on a key. Plans and specifications could include the following:

- essential structural features such as the layout of function rooms, escape doors, wall partitions, corridors, stairways, etc (including any fire-resisting structure and fire doors (with or without door closers) provided to protect the escape routes);

- location of refuges and lifts that have been designated suitable for use by disabled people and others who may need assistance to escape in case of fire;

- methods for fighting fire (details of the number, type and location of the firefighting equipment);

- location of manually-operated fire alarm call points and control equipment for fire alarms;

- location of any control rooms and any fire staff posts;

- location of any emergency escape lighting equipment and the exit route signs;

- location of any high-risk areas, equipment or process that must be immediately shut down by staff on hearing the fire alarm;

- location of any automatic firefighting systems, risers and sprinkler control valves;

- location of the main electrical supply switch, the main water shut-off valve and, where appropriate, the main gas or oil shut-off valves; and

- plans and specifications relating to all recent constructions.

This information should be passed on to any later users or owners of the premises.

7.2 Emergency plans

Emergency plan and contingency plans

Your emergency plan should be appropriate to your premises and could include:

- how people will be warned if there is a fire;

- what staff/patients/visitors should do if they discover a fire;

- how the evacuation of the premises should be carried out;

- individual needs/risks relating to individual wards/patients;

- where people should assemble after they have left the premises and procedures for checking whether the premises have been evacuated;

- identification of key escape routes, how people can gain access to them and escape from them to a place of total safety;

- arrangements for fighting the fire;

- the duties and identity of staff who have specific responsibilities if there is a fire;

- arrangements for the safe evacuation of people identified as being especially at risk, such as patients, those with disabilities, contractors and visitors;

- any machines/appliances/processes/power supplies that need to be stopped or isolated if there is a fire;

- specific arrangements, if necessary, for high-fire-risk areas;

- contingency plans for when life safety systems are out of order, e.g. fire-detection and alarm systems, sprinklers or smoke control systems;

- how the fire and rescue service and any other necessary services will be called and who will be responsible for doing this; and

- procedures for meeting the fire and rescue service on their arrival and notifying them of the locations of remaining patients and of any special risks, e.g. the location of highly flammable materials.

As part of your emergency plan it is good practice to prepare post-incident plans for dealing with situations that might arise, such as those involving:

- unaccompanied children;

- people with personal belongings (especially valuables) still in the building;

- people in a state of undress;

- getting people away from the building (e.g. to transport);

- arranging alternative accommodation; and

- inclement weather.

You should therefore prepare contingency plans to determine specific actions and/or the mobilisation of specialist resources.

The emergency services may prepare an emergency procedure plan (or major incident plan) for dealing with a major incident (a large fire). Your contingency plans and the emergency procedure plan should be compatible. In such cases, you should consult with the police, fire and rescue authority, NHS ambulance trust and the appropriate primary care trust, strategic health authority or local authority to produce an agreed, comprehensive plan.

Guidance on developing health and safety management policy has been published by the HSE.[31]

7.3 Information, instruction, co-operation and co-ordination

Supplying information
You must provide easily understandable information to employees, the parents of children you may employ, and to employers of other persons working in your premises about the measures in place to ensure a safe escape from the building and how they will operate, for example:

- any significant risks to staff, patients and other relevant persons that have been identified in your fire risk assessment or any similar assessment carried out by another user and responsible person in the building;

- the fire prevention and protection measures and procedures in your premises and where they impact on staff and other relevant persons in the building;

- the procedures for fighting a fire in the premises; and

- the identity of people who have been nominated with specific responsibilities in the building.

Even if you do not have to record the fire risk assessment, it would be helpful to keep a record of any co-operation and exchange of information made between employers and other responsible people for future reference.

You need to ensure that all staff and, where necessary, other relevant persons who work in the building receive appropriate information in a way that can be easily understood. This might include any special instructions to particular people who have been allocated a specific task, such as shutting down equipment or guiding people to the nearest exit.

Duties of employees to give information
Employees also have a duty to take reasonable care for their own safety and that of other people who may be affected by their activities. This includes the need for them to inform their employer of any activity that they consider would present a serious and immediate danger to their own safety and that of others.

Dangerous substances
HSE publishes guidance[8] about specific substances where appropriate information may need to be provided. If any of these, or any other substance that is not included but nevertheless presents more than a slight risk, is present in your premises, then you must provide such information to staff and others, specifically you must:

- name the substance and the risks associated with it, e.g. how to safely use or store the product to avoid creating highly flammable vapours or explosive atmospheres;

- identify any legislative provisions that may be associated with the substance;

- allow employees access to the hazardous substances safety data sheet; and

- inform the fire and rescue service where dangerous substances are present on the premises.

Information to the fire and rescue services
In addition to providing information to the fire and rescue service when dangerous substances are present in sufficient quantities to pose an enhanced risk, it will also be helpful to inform them of any short-term changes that might have an impact on their firefighting activities,

e.g. in the event of temporary loss of a firefighting facility and temporary alterations.

Procedures should also include meeting and briefing the fire and rescue service when they arrive.

Case study

If the firefighting lift in a large multi-storey hospital becomes defective, this must also be brought to the attention of the fire and rescue service. Being unable to use this facility to tackle a fire on the upper floors might have a serious effect on the ability of firefighters to begin operations as quickly as planned. The information supplied will enable the emergency services to make adjustments to the level of the emergency response.

Instruction

You will need to carefully consider the type of instructions to staff and other people working in your premises. Written instructions must be concise, comprehensible and relevant and therefore must be reviewed and updated as new working practices and hazardous substances are introduced.

Inclusive access and employment policies mean that people with learning difficulties may now be present in a range of premises and your fire risk assessment should consider whether further instruction or guidance is necessary to ensure that your evacuation strategy is appropriate and understood by everyone.

Instructions will need to be given to people delegated to carry out particular tasks, for example:

- regularly checking (and, if necessary, removing) security bolts, bars or chains on final exit doors to ensure that escape routes are accessible;

- daily, weekly, quarterly and yearly checks on the range of fire safety measures (in larger premises some of the work may be contracted out to a specialist company);

- safety considerations at the end of each day, e.g. removing rubbish, ensuring exits are usable and closing fire doors and shutters;

- leaving hazardous substances in a safe condition when evacuating the building;

- the safe storage of hazardous substances at the end of the working day; and

- ensuring everyone knows how to use internal emergency telephones.

Specific instructions may be needed about:

- how staff will help patients and visitors to leave the building;

- 'sweeping' of the floor by staff to guide people to the nearest exit when the fire alarm sounds;

- designating particular areas of the premises for supervisors or staff to check that no one remains inside;

- calling the emergency services;

- carrying out evacuation roll calls;

- taking charge at the assembly area;

- meeting and directing fire engines; and

- cover arrangements when nominated people are on leave.

Co-operation and co-ordination

Where you share premises with others (e.g. as part of a complex), each responsible person, i.e. each employer, owner or other person who has control over any part of the premises, will need to co-operate and co-ordinate the findings of their separate fire risk assessments to ensure the fire precautions and protection measures are effective throughout the building. This could include:

- co-ordinating an emergency plan (see Part 1, Step 4.2 and Part 2, Section 7.2 for features of an emergency plan);

- identifying the nature of any risks and how they may affect others in or about the premises;

- identifying any fire-prevention and protection measures;

- identifying any measures to mitigate the effects of a fire; and

- arranging any contacts with external emergency services and calling the fire and rescue service.

7.4 Fire safety training

Staff training

The actions of staff, if there is a fire, are likely to be crucial to their safety and that of other people in the premises. All staff (including managers and senior staff in all professions) should receive basic fire safety induction training and attend refresher sessions at least once in every 12-month period in accordance with the guidance in HTM 05-01.[82]

Additional training should be provided for the fire safety manager and any deputies. Specific training should also be given to all staff who regularly deal with flammable materials or heat-producing equipment. Similarly, staff involved in the selection, installation, operation and maintenance of fire-detection and alarm systems should be conversant with the requirements of HTM 82[77] and receive adequate training in accordance with the appropriate section of that HTM.

You should ensure that all staff and contractors (and, if appropriate, patients and regular visitors) are told about the emergency plan and are shown the escape routes. Where certain services (catering, cleaning, etc) are provided by contractors, the availability of staff to assist with patient evacuation may be limited. Where contractors are required to assist with patient evacuation, it is essential that it is discussed and agreed, and then stated in the contract.

The training should take account of the findings of the fire risk assessment and be easily understood by all those attending. It should include the role that those members of staff will be expected to carry out if a fire occurs. This may vary in large premises, with some staff being appointed as fire marshals or being given some other particular role for which additional training will be required.

In addition to the guidance given in Part 1, Step 4.4, as a minimum all staff should receive training on:

- the items listed in your emergency plan, including;

  - the correct action to be taken when a fire is discovered;

  - evacuation and escape procedures;

- the importance of fire doors and other basic fire-safety measures;

- where relevant, the appropriate use of firefighting equipment (including demonstrations);

- the importance of reporting to the assembly area;

- exit routes and the operation of exit devices, including physically walking these routes;

- general matters such as permitted smoking areas or restrictions on cooking other than in designated areas; and

- assisting disabled persons where necessary.

Training is necessary:

- when staff start employment or are transferred into the premises;

- when changes have been made to the emergency plan and the preventive and protective measures;

- where working practices and processes or people's responsibilities change;

- to take account of any changed risks to the safety of staff or other relevant persons;

- to ensure that staff know what they have to do to safeguard themselves and others on the premises; and

- where staff are expected to assist disabled persons.

In situations where patients of poor mobility are to be physically moved by staff, you must ensure that the staff have received the appropriate training to do so. If evacuation aids or equipment is provided for this purpose, staff should be trained to deploy and utilise them as quickly and efficiently and with as little distress to the patient as possible. Determination of acceptable escape times depends on all of the above, and no single factor should be considered in isolation. The ability of staff to conduct an evacuation of each protected area within a short period of time is a starting point upon which to make an assessment. Extended escape time may be able to be dealt with by careful adjustment to the above factors.

Alternatively, fire-engineering solutions may be available to compensate for extended escape time, but should only be considered following the advice from a competent person.

Training should be repeated as often as necessary (at least once in every 12-month period) and should take place during the working hours of individual staff members.

Whatever training you decide is necessary to support your fire safety strategy and emergency plan, it should be verifiable.

Records kept of training should include:

- the date of the training;

- the duration;

- the name of the person giving the training;

- the names of the people receiving the training; and

- the nature of the training.

Enforcing authorities may want to examine records as evidence that adequate training has been given.

Fire wardens

Staff expected to undertake the role of fire wardens (sometimes called fire marshals) would require more comprehensive training. Their role may include:

- helping any members of the public, visitors and/or disabled persons to leave the premises;

- checking designated areas to ensure everyone has left;

- using firefighting equipment if safe to do so;

- liaising with the fire and rescue service on arrival;

- shutting down vital or dangerous equipment; and

- performing a supervisory/managing role in any fire situation.

Training for this role may include:

- detailed knowledge of the fire safety strategy of the premises;

- awareness of human behaviour in fires;

- how to encourage others to use the most appropriate escape route;

- how to search safely and recognise areas that are unsafe to enter;

- the difficulties that some people, particularly if disabled, may have in escaping and any special evacuation arrangements that have been pre-planned;

- additional training in the use of firefighting equipment;

- an understanding of the purpose of any fixed firefighting equipment such as sprinklers or gas flooding systems; and

- reporting of faults, incidents and near misses.

Fire drills

Once the emergency plan has been developed and training given, you will need to evaluate its effectiveness. The best way to do this is to perform a fire drill. This should be carried out at least annually or as determined by your fire risk assessment. For example, if you have a high staff turnover, you may need to carry them out more often.

A well-planned and executed fire drill will confirm understanding of the training and provide helpful information for future training. The responsible person should determine the possible objectives of the drill, such as to:

- identify any weaknesses in the evacuation strategy;

- test the procedure following any recent alteration or changes to working practices;

- familiarise new members of staff with procedures;

- familiarise patients with procedures; and

- test the arrangements for disabled people.

Who should take part?

Within each building the evacuation should include all occupants except those who may need to ensure the security of the premises, or people who, on a risk-assessed basis, cannot be moved, must remain with a patient who cannot be moved, or are required to remain with particular equipment or processes that cannot be closed down.

Premises or complexes that consist of several buildings on the same site should be dealt with one building at a time over an appropriate period unless the emergency procedure dictates otherwise.

You should consider the feasibility of drills involving non-ambulant or semi-ambulant patients. Where safe to do so, drills may include patients, or a significant number of patients. It is advisable to either have one drill at night or to simulate night-time conditions, which would include the applicable night staffing levels, ensuring that all necessary health and safety issues are addressed before you do so.

The frequency of drills should ensure that regular occasional patients (e.g. who attend the premises for a few days each month for respite care) are included in some drills.

Carrying out the drill

For premises that have more than one escape route, the escape plan should be designed to evacuate all people on the assumption that one exit or stairway is unavailable because of the fire. This could be simulated by a designated person being located at a suitable point on an exit route. Applying this scenario to different escape routes at each fire drill will encourage individuals to use alternative escape routes which they may not normally use.

When carrying out the drill you might find it helpful to:

- circulate details concerning the drill and inform all staff of their duty to participate. It may not be beneficial to have 'surprise drills' as the health and safety risks introduced may outweigh the benefits;

- 'train' patients with learning difficulties by using special techniques (e.g. visual imagery);

- ensure that equipment can be safely left;

- nominate observers;

- inform the alarm receiving centre if the fire-warning system is monitored. If the fire and rescue service is normally called directly from your premises, ensure that this does not happen;

- inform visitors if they are present; and

- ask a member of staff at random to set off the alarm by operating the nearest alarm call point using the test key. This will indicate the level of knowledge regarding the location of the nearest call point.

More detailed information on fire drills and test evacuations are given in BS 5588-12.[58]

The roll call/checking the premises have been evacuated

Carry out a roll call as soon as possible at the designated assembly point(s) and/or receive reports from wardens designated to sweep the premises. You should note any people who are unaccounted for. In a real evacuation this information will need to be passed to the fire and rescue service on arrival.

Once the roll call is complete or the reports have been received, allow people to return to the building. If the fire-warning system is monitored, inform the alarm receiving centre that the drill has now been completed and record the outcomes of the drill.

In premises where patients may not be fully aware of what is happening (due to age or mental impairment), staff will have to act on their behalf. It is also possible that some patients will wander away from the assembly point and this should be monitored and, if possible, controlled.

Monitoring and debrief

Throughout the drill the responsible person and nominated observers should pay particular attention to:

- difficulties in moving, or the time taken to move, non- or semi-ambulant patients;

- communication difficulties with regard to the roll call and establishing that everyone is accounted for;

- the use of the nearest available escape routes as opposed to common circulation routes;

- difficulties with the opening of final exit doors;

- difficulties experienced by people with disabilities;

- the roles of specified people, e.g. fire wardens;

- inappropriate actions, e.g. stopping to collect personal items, attempting to use lifts, etc; and

- windows and doors not being closed as people leave.

On-the-spot debriefs are useful to discuss the fire drill, encouraging feedback from everybody. Later, reports from fire wardens and observations from people should be collated and reviewed. Any conclusions and remedial actions should be recorded and implemented.

Section 8 Quality assurance of fire protection equipment and installation

Fire protection products and related services should be fit for their purpose and properly installed and maintained in accordance with the manufacturer's instructions or the relevant British Standard.

Third-party certification schemes for fire protection products and related services are an effective means of providing the fullest possible assurances, offering a level of quality, reliability and safety that non-certificated products may lack. This does not mean goods and services that are not third-party approved are less reliable, but there is no obvious way in which this can be demonstrated.

Third-party quality assurance can offer comfort, both as a means of satisfying you that goods and services you have purchased are fit for purpose, and as a means of demonstrating that you have complied with the law.

However, to ensure the level of assurance offered by third-party schemes, you should always check whether the company you employ sub-contracts work to others. If they do, you will want to check that the sub-contractors are subject to the same level of checks of quality and competence as the company you are employing.

Your local fire and rescue service, fire trade associations or your own trade association may be able to provide further details about third-party quality assurance schemes and the various organisations that administer them.

Appendix A

A.1 Example fire safety maintenance checklist

A fire safety maintenance checklist can be used as a means of supporting your fire safety policy. This example list is not intended to be comprehensive and should not be used as a substitute for carrying out a fire risk assessment.

You can modify the example where necessary to fit your premises and may need to incorporate the recommendations of manufacturers and installers of the fire safety equipment/systems that you may have installed in your premises.

Any ticks in the grey boxes should result in further investigation and appropriate action as necessary. In larger and more complex premises you may need to seek the assistance of a competent person to carry out some of the checks.

	Yes	No	N/A	Comments
Daily checks (not normally recorded)				
Escape routes				
Can all fire exits be opened immediately and easily?	☐	☐	☐	
Are fire doors clear of obstructions?	☐	☐	☐	
Are escape routes clear?	☐	☐	☐	
Fire warning systems				
Is the indicator panel showing 'normal'?	☐	☐	☐	
Are whistles, gongs or air horns in place?	☐	☐	☐	
Escape lighting				
Are luminaires and exit signs in good condition and undamaged?	☐	☐	☐	
Is emergency lighting and sign lighting working correctly?	☐	☐	☐	
Firefighting equipment				
Are all fire extinguishers in place?	☐	☐	☐	
Are fire extinguishers clearly visible?	☐	☐	☐	
Are vehicles blocking fire hydrants or access to them?	☐	☐	☐	
Weekly checks				
Escape routes				
Do all emergency fastening devices to fire exits (push bars and pads, etc.) work correctly?	☐	☐	☐	
Are external routes clear and safe?	☐	☐	☐	
Fire warning systems				
Does testing a manual call point send a signal to the indicator panel? (Disconnect the link to the receiving centre or tell them you are doing a test.)	☐	☐	☐	
Did the alarm system work correctly when tested?	☐	☐	☐	
Did staff and other people hear the fire alarm?	☐	☐	☐	
Did any linked fire protection systems operate correctly? (e.g. magnetic door holder released, smoke curtains drop)	☐	☐	☐	

	Yes	No	N/A	Comments
Weekly checks *continued*				
Do all visual alarms and/or vibrating alarms and pagers (as applicable) work?	☐	☐	☐	
Do voice alarm systems work correctly? Was the message understood?	☐	☐	☐	
Escape lighting				
Are charging indicators (if fitted) visible?	☐	☐	☐	
Firefighting equipment				
Is all equipment in good condition?	☐	☐	☐	
Additional items from manufacturer's recommendations.	☐	☐	☐	
Monthly checks				
Escape routes				
Do all electronic release mechanisms on escape doors work correctly? Do they 'fail safe' in the open position?	☐	☐	☐	
Do all automatic opening doors on escape routes 'fail safe' in the open position?	☐	☐	☐	
Are fire door seals and self-closing devices in good condition?	☐	☐	☐	
Do all roller shutters provided for fire compartmentation work correctly?	☐	☐	☐	
Are external escape stairs safe?	☐	☐	☐	
Do all internal self-closing fire doors work correctly?	☐	☐	☐	
Escape lighting				
Do all luminaires and exit signs function correctly when tested?	☐	☐	☐	
Have all emergency generators been tested? (Normally run for one hour.)	☐	☐	☐	
Firefighting equipment				
Is the pressure in 'stored pressure' fire extinguishers correct?	☐	☐	☐	
Additional items from manufacturer's recommendations.	☐	☐	☐	
Three-monthly checks				
General				
Are any emergency water tanks/ponds at their normal capacity?	☐	☐	☐	
Are vehicles blocking fire hydrants or access to them?	☐	☐	☐	
Additional items from manufacturer's recommendations.	☐	☐	☐	
Six-monthly checks				
General				
Has any firefighting or emergency evacuation lift been tested by a competent person?	☐	☐	☐	
Has any sprinkler system been tested by a competent person?	☐	☐	☐	
Have the release and closing mechanisms of any fire-resisting compartment doors and shutters been tested by a competent person?	☐	☐	☐	
Fire warning system				
Has the system been checked by a competent person?	☐	☐	☐	

	Yes	No	N/A	Comments
Six-monthly checks *continued*				
Escape lighting				
Do all luminaires operate on test for one third of their rated value?	☐	☐	☐	
Additional items from manufacturer's recommendations.	☐	☐	☐	
Annual checks				
Escape routes				
Do all self-closing fire doors fit correctly?	☐	☐	☐	
Is escape route compartmentation in good repair?	☐	☐	☐	
Escape lighting				
Do all luminaires operate on test for their full rated duration?	☐	☐	☐	
Has the system been checked by a competent person?	☐	☐	☐	
Firefighting equipment				
Has all firefighting equipment been checked by a competent person?	☐	☐	☐	
Miscellaneous				
Has any dry/wet rising fire main been tested by a competent person?	☐	☐	☐	
Has the smoke and heat ventilation system been tested by a competent person?	☐	☐	☐	
Has external access for the fire service been checked for ongoing availability?	☐	☐	☐	
Have any firefighters' switches been tested?	☐	☐	☐	
Has the fire hydrant bypass flow valve control been tested by a competent person?	☐	☐	☐	
Are any necessary fire engine direction signs in place?	☐	☐	☐	

A2 Example form for recording significant findings

Risk Assessment – Record of significant findings	
Risk assessment for	**Assessment undertaken by**
Building	Date
	Completed by
Location	Signature
Floor level	**Use**

Step 1 – Identify fire hazards		
Sources of ignition	**Sources of fuel**	**Sources of oxygen**

Step 2 – People at risk

Step 3 – Evaluate, remove, reduce and protect from risk

(3.1) Evaluate the risk of the fire occuring

(3.2) Evaluate the risk to people from a fire starting in the premises

(3.3) Remove and reduce the hazards that may cause a fire

(3.4) Remove and reduce the risks to people from a fire

Assessment review		
Assessment review date	**Completed by**	**Signature**

Review outcome (where substantial changes have occurred a new record sheet should be used)

Notes:
(1) The risk assessment record of significant findings should refer to other plans, records or other documents as necessary.
(2) The information in this record should assist you to develop an emergency plan; co-ordinate measures with other 'responsible persons' in the building; and to inform and train staff and inform other relevant persons.

Appendix B

Technical information on fire-resisting separation, fire doors and door fastenings

B1 Fire-resisting separation

General

The materials from which your premises are constructed may determine the speed with which a fire may spread, affecting the escape routes that people will use. A fire starting in a building constructed mainly from readily combustible material will spread faster than one where modern fire-resisting construction materials have been used. Where non-combustible materials are used and the internal partitions are made from fire-resisting materials, the fire will be contained for a longer period, allowing more time for the occupants to escape.

Because of the requirements of building regulations (HTM 81[76] or HTM 05-02: Part A[76]) you will probably already have some walls and floors that are fire-resisting and limitations on the surface finishes to certain walls and ceilings.

You will need to consider whether the standard of fire resistance and surface finishing in the escape routes is satisfactory, has been affected by wear and tear or alterations and whether any improvements are necessary.

The following paragraphs give basic information on how fire-resisting construction can provide up to 30 minutes' protection to escape routes. This is the standard recommended for most situations. If you are still unsure of the level of fire resistance which is necessary after reading this information, you should consult a fire safety expert.

For complex healthcare premises, the minimum period of fire resistance provided by the elements of structure is:

Single-storey premises	30 minutes
Premises with floors between one and four storey heights above ground	60 minutes
Premises with floors above four storey heights above ground	90 minutes
Premises with basements two or more storeys deep	90 minutes

Fire-resisting construction

The fire resistance of a wall or floor is dependent on the quality of construction and materials used. Common examples of types of construction that provide 30-minute fire resistance to escape routes if constructed to the above standards are:

- internal framed construction wall, non-load bearing, consisting of 72mm x 37mm timber studs at 600mm centres and faced with 12.5mm of plasterboard with all joints taped and filled (see Figure 63);

- internal framed construction, non-load bearing, consisting of channel section steel studs at 600mm centres faced with 12.5mm of plasterboard with all joints taped and filled; and

- masonry cavity wall consisting of solid bricks of clay, brick earth, shale, concrete or calcium silicate, with a minimum thickness of 90mm on each leaf.

There are other methods and products available which will achieve the required standard of fire resistance and may be more appropriate for the existing construction in your premises. If there is any doubt about how your building is constructed, then ask for further advice from a competent person.

Fire-resisting floors

The fire resistance of floors will depend on the existing floor construction as well as the type of ceiling finish beneath. If you need to upgrade the fire resistance of your floor it may not be desirable to apply additional fire resistance to the underside of an existing ornate ceiling. In older buildings there may be a requirement to provide fire resistance between beams and joists.

A typical example of a 30-minute fire-resisting timber floor is tongue and groove softwood of not less than 15mm finished thickness on 37mm timber joists, with a ceiling below of one layer of plasterboard to a thickness of 12.5mm with joints taped and filled and backed by supporting timber.

Figure 63: Fire-resisting construction

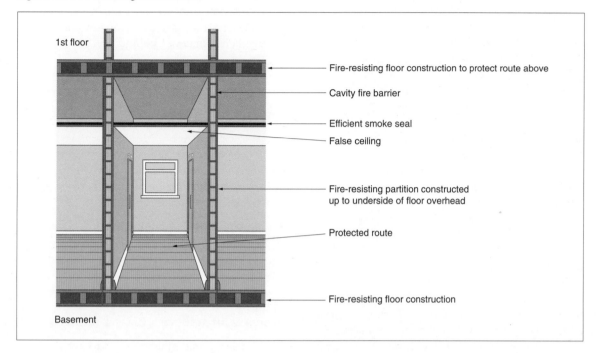

There are other, equally valid, methods and products available for upgrading floors. If you are in any doubt you should ask the advice of a competent person and ensure that the product is installed in accordance with instructions from the manufacturer or supplier.

Fire-resisting glazing

The most common type of fire-resisting glazing is 6mm Georgian wired glazing, which is easily identifiable. Clear fire-resisting glazing is available and can quickly be identified by a mark etched into the glass, usually in the corner of the glazed panel, to confirm its fire-resisting standard. Although this is not compulsory, the marking of glass is supported by the Glass and Glazing Federation; you should check whether the glazing will be marked accordingly before purchase. The glazing should have been installed in accordance with the manufacturer's instructions and to the appropriate standard,[60] to ensure that its fire-resisting properties are maintained.

For healthcare premises greater than 12m in height, the guidance in the BRE guide[34] should be followed.

The performance of glazed systems in terms of fire resistance and external fire exposure should, wherever possible, be confirmed by test evidence. Alternatively, where there is a lack of test information, ask for an assessment of the proposed construction from suitably qualified people.

Fire separation of voids

A common problem encountered with fire separation is fire-resisting partitions which do not extend above false ceilings to true ceiling height. This may result in unseen fire spread and a loss of vital protection to the escape routes. It is important therefore to carefully check all such partitions have been installed correctly.

CLASP and SCOLA type construction

CLASP (Consortium of Local Authorities Special Programme) and SCOLA (Second Consortium of Local Authorities) are total or systematic methods of construction that were developed to provide consistent building quality, while reducing the need for traditional skilled labour. They consist of a metal frame upon which structural panels are fixed. This results in hidden voids through which fire may spread. It is important that cavity barriers that restrict the spread of fire are installed appropriately, especially to walls and floors that need to be fire-resisting. If you are in any doubt as to whether any remedial work will be required, then ask for advice from a competent person.

Breaching fire separation

To ensure effective protection against fire, walls and floors providing fire separation must form a complete barrier, with an equivalent level of fire resistance provided to any openings such as doors, ventilation ducts, pipe passages or refuse chutes.

The passing of services such as heating pipes or electrical cables through fire-resisting partitions leaves gaps through which fire and smoke may spread. This should be rectified by suitable fire stopping and there are many proprietary products available to suit particular types of construction. Such products should be installed by competent contractors.

Décor and surface finishes of walls, ceilings and escape routes

The finish applied to walls and ceilings can contribute to the spread of fire. Some finishes will transfer fire from one area to another very quickly by surface spread of flame. This not only makes the fire difficult to control, but provides additional fuel, which will increase the severity of the fire.

Surface finishes used in various locations throughout healthcare premises should therefore meet appropriate levels of fire performance. Fire performance is classified either by product performance or by surface spread of flame rating.

Class 0 is the highest product performance classification but is not a classification identified in any British Standard test. Class 0 is defined in Approved Document B of the Building Regulations[24].

Surface finishes that can be effectively tested for surface spread of flame are rated for performance by reference to the method specified in BS 476-7.[32] Under this standard, materials or products are classified 1, 2, 3 or 4, with Class 1 being the highest.

The classes normally used in healthcare premises are Class 0 or Class 1, and the following table gives guidance on classifications for use in specific areas:

Location	Walls	Ceiling
Circulation spaces	Class 0	Class 0
Other rooms	Class 0	Class 1
Small rooms (up to 4m²)	Class 1	Class 1

The following generic materials and products all achieve a Class 0 rating:

- products classified as non-combustible when tested to BS 476-4;[75]

- brickwork, blockwork, concrete and ceramic tiles;

- plasterboard (painted or not, or with a PVC facing not more than 0.5mm thick) with or without an air gap or fibrous or cellular insulating material behind;

- wood-wool cement slabs; and

- mineral fibre tiles or sheets with cement or resin binding.

The following materials may also achieve Class 0 but, as the properties of different products with the same generic description vary, the ratings of these materials/products should be substantiated by test evidence:

- aluminium-faced fibre insulating boards, flame-retardant decorative laminates on calcium silicate board, thick polycarbonate sheet, phenolic sheet and UPVC.

The following generic materials and products all achieve a Class 1 rating:

- all Class 0 materials referred to above plus timber, hardboard, blockboard, particle board, heavy flock wallpapers and thermosetting plastics if flame-retardant treated to achieve a Class 1 standard.

The following materials may also achieve Class 1 but, as the properties of different products with the same generic description vary, the ratings of these materials/products should be substantiated by test evidence:

- phenolic or melamine laminates on a calcium silicate substrate and flame-retardant decorative laminates on a combustible core.

Additional finishes

Where walls are covered by temporary surfaces (such as posters, fabrics, prints, decorations, etc), the significance of these needs to be considered.

Small areas with finishes with a lower classification than specified may be acceptable provided they do not amount to more than 5% of the total wall area (for example notice boards).

Where walls have been subject to repeated painting over a number of years with gloss paints, the accumulated thickness of paint film may present a high fire hazard and provide for rapid transfer of fire over its surface. Where this situation exists, specialist technical advice should be obtained. The use of anti-graffiti and intumescent paints requires careful consideration, especially when they are applied over existing painted surfaces. Full technical guidance should always be obtained from the manufacturer.

Floor coverings

The finish applied to a floor may also contribute to the spread of fire. HTM 61[90] gives guidance on the selection of floor finishes for hospitals.

Although hardwood flooring is not considered a fire hazard, the finish applied to certain flooring materials may, over a period of time, accumulate and constitute a fire hazard. The accumulation, over a number of years, of wax polish applied to a timber floor will pose a significant fire hazard.

Standards

European classifications, are an acceptable alternative to national classifications but it should be noted that national classifications do not always automatically equate with the equivalent European classification. Further guidance about internal linings, including guidance on classifications, is available in Approved Document B,[24] HTM 81[76] and HTM 85.[79]

Note: The higher classifications quoted in the HTMs (and listed in the table above) should be used in place of those quoted in Approved Document B.[24]

Appropriate testing procedures are detailed in BS 476-7[32] and, where appropriate, BS EN 13501-1.[33]

Further guidance on types of fire-resisting construction has been published by the Building Research Establishment.[34]

B2 Fire-resisting doors

Requirements of a fire-resisting door

Effective fire-resisting doors (see Figure 64) are vital to ensure that the occupants can evacuate to a place of safety. Correctly specified and well-fitted doors will hold back fire and smoke, preventing escape routes becoming unusable, as well as preventing the fire spreading from one area to another.

Fire-resisting doors are necessary in any doorway located in a fire-resisting structure. Most internal doors are constructed of timber. These will give some limited protection against fire spread, but only a purpose-built fire-resisting door that has been tested to an approved standard will provide the necessary protection. Metal fire-resisting doors are also available and specific guidance for these follows.

All fire-resisting doors are rated by their performance when tested to an appropriate standard. The level of protection provided by the door is measured, primarily by determining the time taken for a fire to breach the integrity (E), of the door assembly, together with its resistance to the passage of hot gases and flame.

It may be possible to upgrade the fire resistance of existing doors. Further information is available from the Building Research Establishment (BRE)[61] or Timber Research and Development Association (TRADA).[62]

Timber fire-resisting doors require a gap of 2–4mm between the door leaf and the frame. However, larger gaps may be necessary to ensure that the door closes flush into its frame when smoke seals are fitted. Further information is available in BS 4787-1.[63] For fire-resisting purposes the gap is normally protected by installing an intumescent seal, in either the door or, preferably, the frame. The intumescent seal expands in the early stages of a fire and enhances the protection given by the door. Additional smoke seals, either incorporated in the intumescent seal or fitted separately, will restrict the spread of smoke at ambient temperatures. Doors fitted with smoke seals have their classification code suffixed with an 'S'.

The principal fire-resisting door categories are:

- E20 fire-resisting door providing 20 minutes fire resistance (or equivalent FD 20S) (Note: Many suppliers no longer provide an E 20 type fire-resisting door).

- E30 fire-resisting door providing 30 minutes fire resistance (or equivalent FD 30S).

- E60 fire-resisting door providing 60 minutes fire resistance (or equivalent FD 60S).

Timber fire-resisting doors are available that will provide up to 120 minutes fire resistance but their use is limited to more specialised conditions that are beyond the scope of this guidance.

Metal fire-resisting doors

Although the majority of fire-resisting doors are made from timber, metal fire-resisting doors, which meet the appropriate standard, can often be used for the same purpose. However, there are situations, especially in healthcare premises, where they are more appropriate. The majority of metal fire-resisting door manufacturers will require the use of bespoke frames and hardware for their door sets.

See BS EN 1634-1[35] and BS 476-22[36] for more information.

For detailed guidance refer to Approved Document B.[24]

Glazing in fire-resisting doors

Although glazing provides additional safety in everyday use and can enhance the appearance of fire-resisting doors, it should never reduce the fire resistance of the door. The opening provided in the door for the fire-resisting glazing unit(s), the fitting of a proven intumescent glazing system and the fitting of the beading are critical, and should only be entrusted to a competent person. In all cases the door and glazing should be purchased from a reputable supplier who can provide documentary evidence that the door continues to achieve the required rating.

Fire-resisting door furniture

Hinges

To ensure compliance with their rated fire performance, fire-resisting doors must be hung with the correct number, size and quality of hinges. Normally a minimum of three hinges are needed; however, the manufacturer's instructions should be closely followed. BS EN 1935,[37] including Annex B, is the appropriate standard.

Alternative door mountings

Although the most common method of hanging a door is to use single axis hinges, alternative methods are employed where the door is required to be double swing or mounted on pivots for other reasons.

Floor-mounted controlled door-closing devices are the most common method regularly found with timber, glass and steel doors, while transom-mounted devices are commonly used with aluminium sections. In each case reference should be made to the fire test report for details as to compliance with the composition of the door assembly, including the door-mounting conditions.

Self-closing devices

All fire-resisting doors, other than those to locked cupboards and service ducts, should be fitted with an appropriately controlled self-closing device that will effectively close the door from any angle. In certain circumstances, concealed, jamb-mounted closing devices may be specified and in these cases should be capable of closing the door from any angle and against any latch fitted to the door; spring hinges are unlikely to be suitable. Further information is available in BS EN 1154.[38]

Rising butt hinges are not suitable for use as a self-closing device due to their inability to close and latch the door from any angle.

Automatic door hold-open/release devices for self-closing fire doors

These devices are designed to hold open self-closing fire doors or allow them to swing free during normal use. In the event of a fire alarm the device will then release the door automatically, allowing the self-closing mechanism to close the door.

Such devices are particularly useful in situations where self-closing doors on escape routes are used regularly by significant numbers of people, or by people with impaired mobility who may have difficulty in opening the doors.

Typical examples of such devices include:

- electromagnetic devices fitted to the fire-resisting door which release when the fire-detection and warning system operates, allowing a separate self-closer to close the door;

- electromagnetic devices within the controlled door-closing device which function on the operation of the fire-detection and warning system; and

- 'free swing' controlled door-closing devices, which operate by allowing the door leaf to work independently of the closing device in normal conditions. An electromagnetic device within the spring mechanism linked to the fire-detection and warning system ensures that the door closes on the operation of the system.

Note: Free swing devices may not be suitable in some situations, such as corridors, where draughts are a problem and the doors are likely to swing uncontrolled, causing possible difficulty or injury to certain people, e.g. those with certain disabilities, the elderly and frail, or young children.

Automatic door-hold open/release devices fitted to doors protecting escape routes should only be installed in conjunction with an automatic fire-detection and warning system incorporating smoke detectors, that is designed to protect the escape routes in the building (see Part 2, Section 2).

In all cases the automatic device should release the fire-resisting door, allowing it to close effectively within its frame when any of the following conditions occur:

- the detection of smoke by an automatic detector;

- the actuation of the fire-detection and alarm system by manual means, e.g. operation of a break-glass call point;

- any failure of the fire detection and alarm system; or

- any electrical power failure.

Other devices, including self-contained devices which perform a similar function, that are not connected directly to a fire alarm system and are not therefore able to meet the above criteria are available and may be acceptable where a site-specific risk assessment can show that they are appropriate. Such devices are unlikely to be suitable for use on doors protecting single stairways or other critical means of escape.

In all cases where a door hold-open device is used, it should be possible to close the door manually.

A site-specific risk assessment should be undertaken before any type of automatic door hold-open/release device is installed. If you are unsure about the suitability of such devices in your premises, you should seek the advice of a competent person.

Further guidance about automatic door hold open/release devices is given in BSEN 1155[65] or BS 5839-3.[39]

Door co-ordinators
Where pairs of doors with rebated meeting stiles are installed, it is critical that the correct closing order is maintained. Door co-ordinators to BS EN 1158[66] should be fitted and fully operational in all cases where the doors are self-closing.

Installation and workmanship
The reliability and performance of correctly specified fire-resisting doors can be undermined by inadequate installation. It is important that installers with the necessary level of skill and knowledge are used. Accreditation schemes for installers of fire-resisting doors are available.

Figure 64: A fire door with smoke seals and infumescent strips

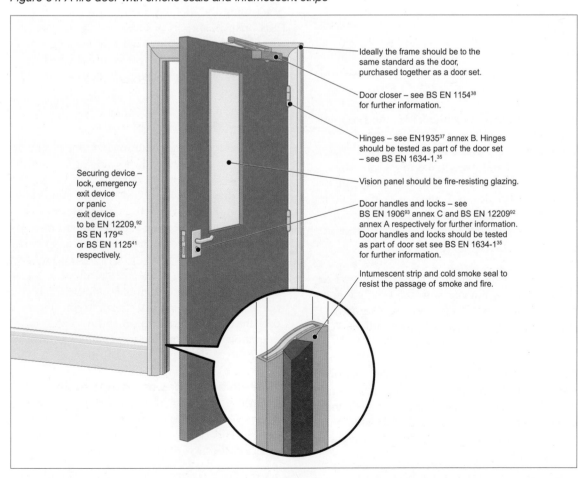

Securing device – lock, emergency exit device or panic exit device to be EN 12209,[92] BS EN 179[42] or BS EN 1125[41] respectively.

Ideally the frame should be to the same standard as the door, purchased together as a door set.

Door closer – see BS EN 1154[38] for further information.

Hinges – see EN1935[37] annex B. Hinges should be tested as part of the door set – see BS EN 1634-1.[35]

Vision panel should be fire-resisting glazing.

Door handles and locks – see BS EN 1906[93] annex C and BS EN 12209[92] annex A respectively for further information. Door handles and locks should be tested as part of door set see BS EN 1634-1[35] for further information.

Intumescent strip and cold smoke seal to resist the passage of smoke and fire.

Fire-resisting doors and shutters will require routine maintenance, particularly to power operation and release and closing mechanisms.

Further information is available on fire-resisting doors in BS 8214.[40] If you are unsure about the quality, the effectiveness or the fitting of your fire-resisting doors, consult a fire safety expert.

For further guidance on the selection and maintenance of door furniture suitable for use on timber fire-resisting and escape doors, refer to the Door and Hardware Federation/Guild of Architectural Ironmongers Code of Practice.[67]

B3 Door-fastening devices

The relationship between the securing of doors against unwanted entry and the ability to escape through them easily in an emergency has often proved problematical. Careful planning and the use of quality materials remain the most effective means of satisfying both of these objectives.

Any device that impedes people making good their escape, either by being unnecessarily complicated to manipulate or not being readily openable, will not be acceptable.

Guidance on fire exits starts from the position that doors on escape routes should not be fitted with any locking devices (electrically operated or otherwise). However, it is accepted that in many cases the need for security will require some form of device that prevents unlimited access but still enables the occupants of a building or area to open the door easily if there is a fire. These devices can take many forms but, in the majority of cases, premises where there are members of the public present or others who are not familiar with the building should use panic exit bar devices (i.e. push bars or touch bars). For further information see BS EN 1125.[41]

Premises that have limited numbers of staff or others who are familiar with the building and where panic is not likely may use alternative devices (i.e. push pads or lever handles). For further information see BS EN 179.[42]

In some larger premises, when only certain staff are on the premises and there is a security issue, it may be acceptable to restrict the number of emergency exits immediately available, e.g. when only security staff are present at night or prior to opening the premises in the morning. Staff should be made fully aware of any restrictions and the number of exits not immediately available should be limited.

Electrical locking devices

Electrically operated entry control devices have been developed for use as locking devices on fire exits. They fall into two main categories, electromechanical and electromagnetic.

• Electromechanical devices

Electromechnical devices comprise electromechanical lock keeps and draw bolts, which can be controlled by people inside the premises by entering a code or by using 'smart cards', which have been adapted to control the exit from certain areas. These devices have been fitted in many premises and may be linked to the fire-detection and/or warning system. Experience has shown that these devices can fail to open in a number of ways. They are dependent on a spring mechanism to return the lock keep or draw bolt(s) and are liable to jam when pressure is applied to the door. It is also relatively easy to fit them incorrectly. Electromechanical locking devices are normally unacceptable on escape doors, unless they are fitted with a manual means of overriding the locking mechanism such as a push bar, push pad or lever handle, or they do not rely on a spring mechanism, fail-safe open and are not affected by pressure, in which case the criteria for electromagnetic devices should be applied.

• Electromagnetic devices

These devices comprise a magnet and a simple fixed retaining plate with no moving parts and are therefore generally considered to be more reliable due to their inherent 'fail-safe unlocked' operation. Electromagnetic locking devices go some way to addressing the particular concerns surrounding electromechanical locking systems. The release of this type of device is controlled by the interruption of electrical current to an electromagnet, either manually via a switch or other means, a break-glass point (typically coloured green and with an alarm to alert operation), or by linking to the fire-warning and/or detection system of the premises.

Time-delay devices on escape routes

A further development is the fitting of a time-delay system to the electronic door-locking device. This delays the actual opening of an exit door for a variable period following operation of the panic bar or other exit device. Periods of between five and 60 seconds can be pre-set at the manufacturing stage or can be adjusted when fitted. These are not normally acceptable for use by members of the public. However, they may be acceptable for use by staff who are familiar with their operation and are suitably trained in their use.

Management of electronic door-control devices including time delays

The use of such devices may be accepted by enforcing authorities if the responsible person can demonstrate, through a suitable risk assessment for each individual door, both the need and the adequate management controls to ensure that people can escape safely from the premises. In particular:

- Access control should not be confused with exit control. Many devices are available which control the access to the premises but retain the immediate escape facility from the premises.

- In public areas, when push bars are operated on escape doors, they should release the electromagnetic locks immediately and allow the exit doors to open.

- The requirement for exit control should be carefully assessed and should not be seen as a substitute for good management of the employees and occupants.

- All other alternatives should have been explored/evaluated prior to using these devices to ensure they do not affect the safety of occupants.

- The device should be connected to the fire-warning and/or detection system.

- The device should incorporate a bypass circuit for immediate release on activation of the fire-warning and/or detection system.

- Each door should be fitted with a single securing device.

- The emergency exit doors should be clearly labelled about how to operate them.

- Adequate control measures should be put in place to ensure the safety of the occupants.

The use of electronic door-locking devices should be considered with particular care in premises with a number of different occupancies. The management of a complicated system of evacuation for many different groups is unlikely to be practicable.

The technical standards in respect of sourcing, maintaining and testing must be extremely high.

When part of the management control system involves trained personnel helping others at these doors, it is vital to ensure these people are available.

The use of exit control devices should not be considered where the number of trained staff is low or where members of the public would be expected to operate the devices without help.

In premises where there may be large numbers of people, the devices should only be considered when linked to a comprehensive automatic fire-detection and warning system in accordance with BS 5839-1.[16] There should be an additional means of manually overriding the locking device at each such exit (typically a green break-glass point).

The use of time-delay systems that prevent the opening of emergency exits for a pre-set time are primarily used to improve security. These add a further layer of complexity to the fire strategy and should not be considered in public areas. They should only be used in non-public areas when all other options such as relocating valuable stock or exterior boundary management have been addressed. Their value in preventing theft is likely to be transient as the use of the manual override becomes more widely known.

BS 8220-3[43] gives further advice on security in buildings and, while this standard does refer to electronic locking devices, it also acknowledges that the balance must remain on the side of emergency escape rather than security.

Appendix C
Historic buildings

General considerations

This appendix offers additional information about listed and historical buildings.

Fire risk assessments conducted within a listed or historic building will need to ensure that a balance is struck between ensuring sufficient fire safety measures are in place for the safety of people, yet avoiding extensive alterations and helping to maintain the character of the building.

As well as the fire risk assessment it is recommended that a general fire policy statement and manual is compiled. A person must be nominated to take responsibility for all aspects of fire safety. Usually the person charged with the management and control of the premises will be the 'responsible person' under the Order.[1]

The advice and/or consent of a building control body or any other relevant bodies (e.g. English Heritage) should form part of any fire risk assessment that impacts on the character of the building (e.g. replacement of doors, fittings, wooden panelling and décor) or material changes to existing escape routes. An ideal solution is one that is reversible, enabling the historic elements to be reinstated.

A fire safety adviser will be able to suggest alternatives to conventional fire precautions, such as:

* a fire engineering solution;

* upgrading existing doors and partitions in a sympathetic manner to improve their fire resistance; and

* considering the installation of specialist fire-detection or suppression systems.

Should the design and nature of the historic building preclude the introduction of conventional fire safety features, it will be necessary to manage the building in such a way that:

* limits the number of occupants, either staff or members of the public, inside the building;

* limits activities in the building; and

* provides adequate supervision within the building.

In buildings that are open to the public, you may wish to designate parts as 'off limits' to the general public. The locking of internal doors or the use of fixed or movable barriers should not restrict alternative escape routes being made available.

Liaison with the fire and rescue service
The responsible person will need to ensure effective liaison with the fire and rescue service to enable them to carry out firefighting operations. These may include information on:

* the provision of water supplies, seasonal ponds, lakes and underground tanks, and any associated pumps;

* difficult access for fire engines;

* particular hazards in the construction features of the building (including asbestos);

* the use of combustible under-floor insulation;

* underground vaults, ducts and voids where fire may spread unchecked;

* worn stone slabs in stairway construction; and

* the presence of cast iron columns and wrought iron beams.

Emergency planning
An important consideration for the owners and trustees is the protection of valuable artefacts and paintings from the effects of fire. However, the efficient evacuation of all occupants must take precedence over procedures for limiting damage to property and contents. Salvage work should be limited to those parts of the building not directly affected by the fire.

Fire wardens and others tasked with carrying out salvage work should have received formal training, adequate protection and be fully briefed about the health and safety risk assessment carried out to identify the dangers associated with this activity.

Further detailed advice on fire safety in historic buildings can found in the following publications:

- BS 7913: *Guide to the principles of the conservation of historic buildings*, British Standards Institution 1988.

- *Heritage under fire: A guide to the protection of historic buildings,* Fire Protection Association (for the UK Working Party on Fire Safety in Historic Buildings) 1991, ISBN 0 902167 94 4.

- *The Installation of Sprinkler Systems in Historic Buildings (Historic Scotland Technical Advice Note S.).* Fire Protection Association (TCRE Division/Scottish Conservation Bureau, Hist.) 1998, ISBN 1 900168 63 4.

- *Fire Protection Measures in Scottish Historic Buildings: Advice on Measures Required to Minimise the Likelihood of Fire Starting and to Alleviate the Destructive Consequences of Fire in Historic Buildings (Technical Advice Note)*, TCRE Division/Scottish Conservation Bureau, Hist. 1997, ISBN 1 900168 41 3.

- *Fire Risk Management in Heritage Buildings (Technical Advice Note)*, TCRE Division/Scottish Conservation Bureau, Hist. 2001, ISBN 1 900168 71 5.

- *Summary and conclusions of the report into fire protection measures for the Royal Palaces* by Sir Alan Bailey, following the Windsor Castle fire, 1992.

- *The fire at Upton Park*, The National Trust.

- *Timber panelled doors and fire*, English Heritage.

- *Fire safety in historic town centres*, English Heritage and Cheshire Fire and Rescue Service.

Appendix D

Glossary

These definitions are provided to assist the responsible person in understanding some of the technical terms used in this guide. They are not exhaustive and more precise definitions may be available in other guidance.

Term	Definition
Access room	A room through which the only escape route from an inner room passes.
Accommodation stairway	A stairway, additional to that required for means of escape purposes, provided for the convenience of occupants.
Alarm receiving station (centre)	An organisation which accepts alarm signals from premises and carries out a pre-determined response.
Alterations notice	If your premises are considered by the enforcing authority to be high-risk, they may issue an alterations notice that requires you to inform them before making any material alterations to your premises.
Alternative escape route	Escape routes sufficiently separated by either direction and space, or by fire-resisting construction to ensure that one is still available irrespective of the location of a fire.
Approved Document B (ADB)[24]	Guidance issued by Government in support of the fire safety aspects of the building regulations.
As low as reasonably practical	Is a concept where risks should continue to be reduced until you reach a point where the cost and effort to reduce the risk further would be grossly disproportionate to the benefit achieved.
Automatic fire-detection system	A means of automatically detecting the products of a fire and sending a signal to a fire-warning system. See 'Fire-warning'.
Automatic fire-suppression system	A firefighting system designed to automatically suppress or extinguish a fire.
Automatic release mechanism	A device that will automatically release either a locking mechanism on an exit route or a hold-open device to a door or roller shutter. It should operate manually or on actuation of the fire-warning or detection system or on failure of the power supply.
Basement	A storey with a floor which at some point is more than 1,200mm below the highest level of ground adjacent to the outside walls, unless, and for escape purposes only, such area has adequate, independent and separate means of escape.
Child	Anyone who is not over compulsory school age, i.e. before or just after their 16th birthday.

Term	Definition
Class 0, 1, 2, 3 or 4 surface spread of flame	Classes of surface spread of flame for materials needed to line walls and ceilings of escape routes. See Appendix B for further information.
Combustible material	A substance that can be burned.
Compartment wall and/or floor	A fire-resisting wall or floor that separates one fire compartment from another.
Competent person	A person with enough training and experience or knowledge and other qualities to enable them properly to assist in undertaking the preventive and protective measures.
Complex healthcare premises	Hospital or other healthcare premises providing invasive procedures and other similar treatments.
Dangerous substance	1. A substance which because of its physico-chemical or chemical properties and the way it is used or is present at the workplace creates a risk. 2. A substance subject to the Dangerous Substances and Explosive Atmosphere Regulations 2002 (DSEAR).[8]
Dead end	Area from which escape is possible in one direction only.
Direct distance	The shortest distance from any point within the floor area to the nearest storey exit, or fire-resisting route, ignoring walls, partitions and fixings.
Domestic premises	Premises occupied as a private dwelling, excluding those areas used in common by the occupants of more than one such dwelling.
Emergency escape lighting	Lighting provided to illuminate escape routes that will function if the normal lighting fails.
Enforcing authority	The fire and rescue authority or any other authority specified in Article 25 of the Regulatory Reform (Fire Safety) Order 2005.[1]
Escape route	Route forming that part of the means of escape from any point in the premises to a final exit.
Evacuation lift	A lift that may be used for the evacuation of people with disabilities, or others, in a fire.
External escape stair	Stair providing an escape route, external to the building.
Fail-safe	Locking an output device with the application of power and having the device unlock when the power is removed. Also known as fail-unlock, remove-action or power- locked.
False alarm	A fire signal, usually from a fire-warning system, resulting from a cause other than fire.
Final exit	An exit from a building where people can continue to disperse in safety and where they are no longer at danger from fire and/ or smoke.

Term	Definition
Fire compartment	A building, or part of a building, constructed to prevent the spread of fire to or from another part of the same building or an adjoining building.
Fire door	A door or shutter, together with its frame and furniture, provided for the passage of people, air or goods which, when closed, is intended to restrict the passage of fire and/or smoke to a predictable level of performance.
Firefighting lift	A lift, designed to have additional protection, with controls that enable it to be used under the direct control of the fire and rescue service when fighting a fire.
Firefighting shaft	A fire-resisting enclosure containing a firefighting stair, fire mains, firefighting lobbies and, if provided, a firefighting lift.
Firefighting stairway	See firefighting shaft.
Fire resistance	The ability of a component or construction of a building to satisfy, for a stated period of time, some or all of the appropriate criteria of relevant standards. (Generally described as 30 minutes fire-resisting or 60 minutes fire-resisting.) See BS EN 1363-1,[44] BS 476-7[32] and associated standards for further information.
Fire safety manager	A nominated person with responsibility for carrying out day-to-day management of fire safety. (This may or may not be the same as the 'responsible person'.)
Fire safety strategy	A number of planned and co-ordinated arrangements designed to reduce the risk of fire and to ensure the safety of people if there is a fire.
Fire stopping	A seal provided to close an imperfection of fit or design tolerance between elements or components, to restrict the passage of fire and smoke.
Fire-warning system	A means of alerting people to the existence of a fire. (See automatic fire-detection system.)
Flammable material	Easily ignited and capable of burning rapidly.
Hazardous substances	1. See Dangerous substance. 2. A substance subject to the Control of Substances Hazardous to Health Regulations 2002 (COSHH).
Healthcare premises	A hospital treatment centre, health centre, clinic, surgery, walk-in centre or other premises where patiets are provided with medical care by a clinician.
Highly flammable	Generally liquids with a flashpoint of below 21°C. (The Chemicals Hazard Information and Packaging for Supply Regulations 2002[45] (CHIP) give more detailed guidance.)

Term	Definition
Hospital street	A Hospital Street is a special type of compartment which connects final exits, stairway enclosures and department entrances and serves as a firefighting bridgehead and a safe evacuation route for occupants to parts of the building unaffected by fire.
Inner room	A room from which escape is possible only by passing through another room (the access room).
Licensed premises	Any premises that require a licence under any statute to undertake trade or conduct business activities.
Material change	An alteration to a building, process or service which significantly affects the level of risk to people from a fire in those premises.
Means of escape	Route(s) provided to ensure safe egress from premises or other locations to a place of total safety.
Phased evacuation	A system of evacuation in which different parts of the premises are evacuated in a controlled sequence of phases, those parts of the premises expected to be at greatest risk being evacuated first.
Place of reasonable safety	A place within a building or structure where, for a limited period of time, people will have some protection from the effects of fire and smoke. This place, usually a corridor, protected area or protected stairway, will normally have a minimum of 30 minutes' fire resistance and allow people to continue their escape to a place of total safety.
Place of total safety	A place, away from the premises, in which people are at no immediate danger from the effects of a fire.
Premises	Any place, such as a building and the immediate land bounded by any enclosure of it, any tent, moveable or temporary structure or any installation or workplace.
Progressive horizontal evacuation	An escape strategy that allows for the horizontal movement of people, from one fire compartment (protected area) to another, away from the fire.
Protected lobby	A fire-resisting enclosure providing access to an escape stairway via two sets of fire doors and into which no room opens other than toilets and lifts.
Protected stairway	A stairway which is adequately protected from the rest of the building by fire-resisting construction.
Protected route	An escape route which is adequately protected from the rest of the building by fire-resisting construction.
Refuge	A place of reasonable safety in which a disabled person or others who may need assistance may rest or wait for assistance before reaching a place of total safety. It should lead directly to a fire-resisting escape route.
Relevant person	Any person lawfully on the premises and any person in the immediate vicinity, but does not include firefighters carrying out firefighting duties.

Term	Definition
Responsible person	The person ultimately responsible for fire safety as defined in the Regulatory Reform (Fire Safety) Order 2005.[1]
Self-closing device	A device that is capable of closing the door from any angle and against any latch fitted to the door.
Significant finding	A feature of the premises, from which the fire hazards and persons at risk are identified. The actions you have taken or will take to remove or reduce the chance of a fire occuring or the spread of fire and smoke. The actions people need to take in case of fire. The necessary information, instruction and training needed and how it will be given.
Simultaneous evacuation	A system of evacuation in which all people evacuate immediately on hearing the fire-warning.
Smoke alarm	Device containing within one housing all the components, except possibly the energy source, for detecting smoke and giving an audible alarm.
Staged fire alarm	A fire warning which can be given in two or more stages for different purposes within a given area (i.e. notifying staff, stand by to evacaute, full evacuation).
Storey exit	A final exit or a doorway giving direct access into a protected stairway, firefighting lobby or external escape route.
Sub-compartment wall and/or floor	A fire-resisting wall or floor that further separates spaces within a fire compartment from another. Typically used to provide temporary refuge during progressive horizontal evacuation of patients within the compartment of fire origin.
Travel distance	The actual distance to be travelled by a person from any point within the floor area to the nearest storey exit or final exit, having regard to the layout of walls, partitions and fixings.
Vision panel	A transparent panel in a wall or door of an inner room enabling the occupant to become aware of a fire in the access area during the early stages.
Way guidance	Low mounted luminous tracks positioned on escape routes in combination with exit indicators, exit marking and intermediate direction indicators along the route, provided for use when the supply to the normal lighting fails, which do not rely on an electrical supply for their luminous output.

Term	Definition
Where necessary	The Order[1] requires that fire precautions (such as firefighting equipment, fire detection and warning, and emergency routes and exits) should be provided (and maintained) 'where necessary'. What this means is that the fire precautions you must provide (and maintain) are those which are needed to reasonably protect relevant people from risks to them in case of fire. This will be determined by the finding of your risk assessment, including the preventative measures you have or will have taken. In practice, it is very unlikely that a properly conducted fire risk assessment, which takes into account all the matters relevant for the safety of people in case of fire, will conclude that no fire precautions (including maintenance) are necessary.
Young person	a. A person aged 16 years, from the date on which he attains that age until and including the 31st August which next follows that date. b. A person aged 16 years and over who is undertaking a course of full-time education at a school or college which is not advanced education. c. A person aged 16 years and over who is undertaking approved training that is not provided through a contract of employment. For the purpose of pargraphs (b) and (c) the person: a. shall have commenced the course of full-time education or approved training before attaining the age of 19 years; and b. shall not have attained the age of 20 years.

Appendix E
Nucleus fire precautions

The objective of the Nucleus fire precaution strategy is to provide life safety, not property protection. Neucleus fire precautions are an integral part of the Nucleus hospital design system. The design strategy provides for the control and containment of a fire as well as for the safe evacuation of patients and other personnel. In common with the Approved Document to Part B of the Building Regulations,[24] HTM 81[76] and HTM 05-02: Part A.[76] it assumes that there will only be one fire at a time within the hospital complex.

There are seven main areas where Nucleus hospitals differ from other hospitals and these are:

- management;

- detection and alarm;

- means of escape;

- fire and smoke containment;

- smoke dispersal;

- separation of fire hazards; and

- firefighting provisions.

The fire precautions in Nucleus hospitals are indicated on standard departmental plans, which were developed by the Department of Health and issued as part of the Nucleus departmental fire plans, in AutoCAD release 13 format, and are included on a CD-ROM with *Fire risk assessment in Nucleus hospitals*.[91]

The Nucleus design provides a high standard of fire safety and, provided all the fire safety measures which were part of the original Nucleus design are maintained and the management aspects of fire safety are acceptable, the overall level of fire safety should be acceptable. For this reason it is important that the original 'as built' fire plans are available.

Nucleus hospitals are those which are designated as conforming to the Nucleus concept by submission to the Department of Health. Such hospitals generally use standard departmental designs with minor modifications agreed locally with the fire authority. In addition to complete hospitals, Nucleus extensions were built to a number of existing hospitals; they are also classified as conforming to the Nucleus principles in the same way.

Some hospitals were built which are loosely termed 'Nucleus related'. The majority of these are located in the area administered by the North West Regional Health Authority. The hospitals use the cruciform template as the basis for planning, but do not fully adopt the Nucleus principles and are not designated by the Department of Health as Nucleus. The fire precautions in these hospitals are designed to comply with HTM 81.[76] Nucleus fire precautions recommendations should not be used in these hospitals.

NHS trusts with hospitals incorporating Nucleus fire precautions should maintain their records and drawings to inform the fire risk assessment of these premises.

References

The following documents are referenced in this guide. Where dated, only this version applies. Where undated, the latest version of the document applies.

1   Regulatory Reform (Fire Safety) Order 2005, SI 2005/1541. The Stationery Office, 2005. ISBN 0 11 072945 5.

2   Fire Precautions Act 1971 (c 40). The Stationery Office, 1971. ISBN 0 10 544071 X.

3   Fire Precautions (Workplace) Regulations 1997, SI 1997/1840. The Stationery Office, 1997. ISBN 0 11 064738 6.

4   Fire Precautions (Workplace) (Amendment) Regulations 1999, SI 1999/1877. The Stationery Office, 1999. ISBN 0 11 082882 8.

5   Health and Safety (Safety Signs and Signals) Regulations 1996, SI 1996/341. The Stationery Office, 1996. ISBN 0 11 054093 X.

6   *Safety signs and signals. The Health and Safety (Safety Signs and Signals) Regulations 1996. Guidance on regulations,* L64. HSE Books, 1996. ISBN 0 7176 0870 0.

7   Dangerous Substances and Explosive Atmospheres Regulations 2002, SI 2002/2776. The Stationery Office, 2002. ISBN 0 11 042957 5.

8   *Dangerous substances and explosive atmospheres. Dangerous Substances and Explosive Atmospheres Regulations 2002. Approved code of practice and guidance,* L138. HSE Books, 2003. ISBN 0 7176 2203 7.

9   *Storage of full and empty LPG cylinders and cartridges. Code of Practice 7.* LP Gas Association, 2000.

10 *Maintaining portable electrical equipment in offices and other low-risk environments,* INDG236. HSE Books, 1996. ISBN 0 7176 1272 4.

11 Construction (Health, Safety and Welfare) Regulations 1996, SI 1996/1592. The Stationery Office, 1996. ISBN 0 11 035904 6.

12 *A guide to the Construction (Health, Safety and Welfare) Regulations 1996,* INDG220 HSE Books, 1996. ISBN 0 7176 1161 2.

     Health and safety in construction, HSG150 (second edition). HSE Books, 2001. ISBN 0 7176 2106 5.

13 Disability Discrimination Act 1995 (c 50). The Stationery Office, 1995. ISBN 0 10 545095 2.

14 BS 8300: *The design of buildings and their approaches to meet the needs of disabled people. Code of practice.* British Standards Institution. ISBN 0 580 38438 1.

15 DCLG/CFOA/BFPSA Guidance on reducing false alarms.

16 BS 5839-1: *Fire-detection and alarm systems for buildings. Code of practice for system design, installation, commissioning and maintenance.* British Standards Institution. ISBN 0 580 40376 9.

17 Manual Handling Operations Regulations 1992, SI 1992/2793. The Stationery Office, 1992. ISBN 0 11 025920 3.

18 BS 5306-8: *Fire extinguishing installations and equipment on premises. Selection and installation of portable fire extinguishers. Code of practice.* British Standards Institution. ISBN 0 580 33203 9.

19 BS 5306-3: *Fire extinguishing installations and equipment on premises. Code of practice for the inspection and maintenance of portable fire extinguishers.* British Standards Institution. ISBN 0 580 42865 6.

20 BS 7863: *Recommendations for colour coding to indicate the extinguishing media contained in portable fire extinguishers.* British Standards Institution. ISBN 0 580 25845 9.

21 BS EN 671-3: *Fixed firefighting systems. Hose systems. Maintenance of hose reels with semi-rigid hose and hose systems with lay-flat hose.* British Standards Institution. ISBN 0 580 34112 7.

22 BS EN 12845: *Fixed firefighting systems. Automatic sprinkler systems. Design, installation and maintenance.* British Standards Institution. ISBN 0 580 44770 7.

23 Workplace (Health, Safety and Welfare) Regulations 1999, SI 1992/3004. The Stationery Office, 1992. ISBN 0 11 025804 5.

24 *The Building Regulations 2000: Approved Document B: Fire safety.* The Stationery Office. ISBN 0 11 753911 2.

25 Local Government (Miscellaneous Provisions) Act 1982 (c 30). The Stationery Office, 1982. ISBN 0 10 543082 X.

26 BS 5395-2: *Stairs, ladders and walkways. Code of practice for the design of industrial type stairs, permanent ladders and walkways.* British Standards Institution. ISBN 0 580 14706 1.

27 BS 5266-8: *Emergency lighting. Code of practice for emergency escape lighting systems.* British Standards Institution.

28 BS 5266-1: *Emergency lighting. Code of practice for the emergency lighting of premises.* British Standards Institution.

29 BS 5499-4: *Safety signs, including fire safety signs. Code of practice for escape route signing.* British Standards Institution.

30 BS 7974: *Application of fire safety engineering principles to the design of buildings. Code of practice.* British Standards Institution. ISBN 0 580 38447 0.

31 *Successful health and safety management,* HSG65 (second edition). HSE Books, 1997. ISBN 0 7176 1276 7.

32 BS 476-7: *Fire tests on building materials and structures. Method of test to determine the classification of the surface spread of flame of products.* British Standards Institution.

33 BS EN 13501-1: *Fire classification of construction products and building elements. Classification using test data from reaction to fire tests.* British Standards Institution.

34 *Guidelines for the construction of fire-resisting structural elements,* BR 128. Building Research Establishment, 1988.

35 BS EN 1634-1: *Fire resistance tests for door and shutter assemblies. Fire doors and shutters.* British Standards Institution. ISBN 0 580 32429 X.

36 BS 476-22: *Fire tests on building materials and structures. Methods for determination of the fire resistance of non-loadbearing elements of construction.* British Standards Institution. ISBN 0 580 15872 1.

37 BS EN 1935: *Building hardware. Single-axis hinges. Requirements and test methods.* British Standards Institution. ISBN 0 580 39272 4.

38 BS EN 1154: *Building hardware. Controlled door closing devices. Requirements and test methods.* British Standards Institution. ISBN 0 580 27476 4.

39 BS 5839-3: *Fire-detection and alarm systems for buildings. Specification for automatic release mechanisms for certain fire protection equipment.* British Standards Institution. ISBN 0 580 15787 3.

40 BS 8214: *Code of practice for fire door assemblies with non-metallic leaves.* British Standards Institution. ISBN 0 580 18871 6.

41 BS EN 1125: *Building hardware. Panic exit devices operated by a horizontal bar. Requirements and test methods.* British Standards Institution.

42 BS EN 179: *Building hardware. Emergency exit devices operated by a lever handle or push pad. Requirements and test methods.* British Standards Institution. ISBN 0 580 28863 3.

43 BS 8220-3: *Guide for security of buildings against crime: Industrial and distribution premises.* British Standards Institution. ISBN 0 580 23692 7.

44 BS EN 1363-1: *Fire resistance tests. General requirements.* British Standards Institution.

45 Chemicals (Hazard Information and Packaging for Supply) Regulations 2002, SI 2002/1689. The Stationery Office, 2002. ISBN 0 11 042419 0.

46 *Guide to the safe warehousing of aerosols.* British Aerosol Manufacturers Association.

47 *Safe use of medical oxygen systems for supply to patients with respiratory disease,* IGC 89/02. European Industrial Gases Association. Internet: www.eiga.org

48 The Electricity at Work Regulations 1989, SI 1989/635. The Stationery Office.

49 The Electrical Equipment (Safety) Regulations 1994, SI 1994/3260. The Stationery Office.

50 The Construction (Design and Management) Regulations 1994 (CONDAM/CDM Regs). The Stationery Office.

51 *Construction Information Sheet: No. 51 Construction fire safety. HSE Books*

52 *Fire safety in construction work,* HSG168. HSE Books. ISBN 0 7176 1332 1.

53 *Fire prevention on construction sites: The joint code of practice on the protection from fire of construction sites and buildings undergoing renovation* (fifth edition). Fire Protection Association and Construction Federation, 2000. ISBN 0 902167 39 1.

54 *Design, construction, specification and fire management of insulated envelopes for temperature controlled environments.* International Association for Cold Storage Construction.

55 Toys (Safety) Regulations 1989, SI 1995/204. The Stationery Office.

56 *CIBSE Guide Volume E: Fire engineering.* Chartered Institution of Building Services Engineers, 1997.

57 *Design methodologies for smoke and heat exhaust ventilation,* Report 368. Building Research Establishment, 1999.

58 BS 5588-12: *Fire precautions in the design, construction and use of buildings. Part 12: Managing fire safety.* British Standards Institution.

59 *The Building Regulations 2000: Approved Document M: Access to and Use of Buildings.* The Stationery Office. ISBN 0 11 703651 X.

60 *A guide to best practice in the specification and use of fire-resistant glazed systems.* Glass and Glazing Federation, 2005.

61 *Increasing the fire resistance of existing timber doors,* Information Paper 8/82. Building Research Establishment.

62 *Fire resisting doorsets by upgrading,* Wood Information Sheet 1-32. Timber Research and Development Association.

63 BS 4787-1: *Internal and external wood doorsets, door leaves and frames. Specification for dimensional requirements.* British Standards Institution.

64 BS 5588-8: *Fire precautions in the design, construction and use of buildings. Code of practice for means of escape for disabled people.* British Standards Institution.

65 BS EN 1155: *Building hardware. Electrically powered hold-open devices for swing doors. Requirements and test methods.* British Standards Institution.

66 BS EN 1158: *Building hardware. Door coordinator devices. Requirements and test methods.* British Standards Institution.

67 *Code of practice: Hardware for fire and escape doors.* Door and Hardware Federation/Guild of Architectural Ironmongers.

68 BS 5266-6: *Emergency lighting. Code of practice for non-electrical low mounted way guidance systems for emergency use. Photoluminescent systems.* British Standards Institution.

69 BS 5499-5: *Graphical symbols and signs. Safety signs, including fire safety signs. Signs with specific safety meanings.* British Standards Institution.

70 BS 6651: *Code of practice for the protection of structures against lighting.* British Standards Institution. ISBN 0 580 33042 7.

71 BS 5306-2: *Fire extinguishing installations and equipment on premises. Specification for sprinkler systems.* British Standards Institution.

72 BS 5306-1: *Fire extinguishing installations and equipment on premises. Hydrant systems, hose reels and foam inlets.* British Standards Institution.

73 BS EN 3-7: *Portable fire extinguishers. Characteristics, performance requirements and test methods.* British Standards Institution.

74 *The storage of flammable liquids in containers,* HSG 51. HSE Books, 1998.

75 BS 476-4: *Fire tests on building materials and structures. Non-combustibility tests for materials.* British Standards Institution.

76 Health Technical Memorandum 81: *Fire precautions in new hospitals* (to be replaced by HTM 05-02: Part A: *Guidance to support functional provisions,* for buildings designed or altered after April 2007). Department of Health Firecode. The Stationery Office.

77 Health Technical Memorandum 82: *Alarm and detection systems* (to be replaced by HTM 05-03: Part B: *Fire-detection and alarm systems* from October 2006). Department of Health Firecode. The Stationery Office.

78 Health Technical Memorandum 83 (to be replaced by HTM 05-03: Part A from October 2006). Department of Health Firecode. The Stationery Office.

79 Health Technical Memorandum 85: *Fire precautions in existing hospitals*. Department of Health Firecode. The Stationery Office.

80 Health Technical Memorandum 86: *Fire risk assessment in hospitals*. Department of Health Firecode. The Stationery Office.

81 Health Technical Memorandum 87: *Textiles and furnishings* (to be replaced by HTM 05-03: Part C: *Textiles and furnishings* from April 2007). Department of Health Firecode. The Stationery Office.

82 Health Technical Memorandum 05-01: *Managing healthcare fire safety*. Department of Health Firecode. The Stationery Office.

83 Health Technical Memorandum 2022: *Medical gas pipeline systems*. Department of Health Firecode. The Stationery Office.

84 *DH Firecode: Nucleus fire precautions recommendations*. HMSO, 1989.

85 Fire practice note 6: *Arson prevention and control in healthcare premises* (re-badged as HTM 05-03: Part F from October 2006). Department of Health Firecode. The Stationery Office.

86 Fire practice note 11: *Reducing unwanted fire signals in healthcare premises* (re-badged as HTM 05-03: Part H from October 2006). Department of Health Firecode. The Stationery Office.

87 Health Technical Memorandum 05-03: Part E: *Escape lifts*. Department of Health Firecode. The Stationery Office.

88 Health Technical Memorandum 2007: *Electrical services supply and distribution*. Department of Health Firecode. The Stationery Office.

89 Health Technical Memorandum 2011: *Emergency electrical services*. Department of Health Firecode. The Stationery Office.

90 Health Technical Memorandum 61: *Flooring*. Department of Health Firecode. The Stationery Office.

91 Health Technical Memorandum: *Fire risk assessment in Nucleus hospitals*. Department of Health Firecode. The Stationery Office.

92 BS EN 12209: *Building hardware. Locks and latches. Mechanically operated locks, latches and locking plates*. British Standards Institution.

93 BS EN 1906: *Building hardware. Leaver handles and furniture. Requirements and test methods*. British Standards Institution.

Further reading

The latest versions of all documents listed in this section should be used, including any amendments.

Any views expressed in these documents are not necessarily those of the DCLG.

BS EN 1935	Building hardware. Single-axis hinges. Requirements and test methods. British Standards Institution.
BS 4422	Fire. Vocabulary. British Standards Institution.
BS PD 6512-3	Use of elements of structural fire protection with particular reference to the recommendations given in BS 5588 Fire precautions in the design and construction of buildings. Guide to the fire performance of glass. British Standards Institution.
BS EN 81	Safety rules for the construction and installation of lifts. British Standards Institution.
BS EN 81-70	Safety rules for the construction and installation of lifts. Particular applications for passenger and goods passenger lifts. Accessibility to lifts for persons including persons with disability. British Standards Institution.
BS EN 54-5	Fire-detection and fire alarm systems. Heat detectors. Point detectors. British Standards Institution.
BS EN 54-7	Fire-detection and fire alarm systems. Smoke detectors. Point detectors using scattered light, transmitted light or ionization. British Standards Institution.
BS EN 54-11	Fire-detection and fire alarm systems. Manual call points. British Standards Institution.
BS 5041-1	Fire hydrant systems equipment. Specification for landing valves for wet risers. British Standards Institution.
BS 5041-2	Fire hydrant systems equipment. Specification for landing valves for dry risers. British Standards Institution.
BS 5041-3	Fire hydrant systems equipment. Specification for inlet breechings for dry riser inlets. British Standards Institution.
BS 5041-4	Fire hydrant systems equipment. Specification for boxes for landing valves for dry risers. British Standards Institution.
BS 5041-5	Fire hydrant systems equipment. Specification for boxes for foam inlets and dry riser inlets. British Standards Institution.
BS 9990	Code of practice for non-automatic firefighting systems in buildings. British Standards Institution.
BS 7944	Type 1 heavy duty fire blankets and type 2 heavy duty heat protective blankets. British Standards Institution.

BS ISO 14520-1	Gaseous fire-extinguishing systems. Physical properties and system design. General requirements. British Standards Institution.
BS EN 1838	Lighting applications. Emergency lighting. British Standards Institution. ISBN 0 580 32992 5. British Standards Institution.
BS 5266-6	Emergency lighting. Code of practice for non-electrical low mounted way guidance systems for emergency use. Photoluminescent systems. British Standards Institution.
BS EN 60598-1	Luminaires. General requirements and tests. British Standards Institution.
BS 5499-1	Graphical symbols and signs. Safety signs, including fire safety signs. Specification for geometric shapes, colours and layout. British Standards Institution.
BS EN 1634-2	Fire resistance tests for door and shutter assemblies. Part 2. Fire door hardware. Building hardware for fire-resisting doorsets and openable windows. British Standards Institution. British Standards Institution.
BS EN 1634-3	Fire resistance tests for door and shutter assemblies. Smoke control doors and shutters. British Standards Institution.
BS EN 45020	Standardisation and related activities. General vocabulary. British Standards Institution.
ISO 13784-2	Reaction to fire tests for sandwich panel building systems. Part 2: test method for large rooms. British Standards Institution.
BS 6661	Guide for design, construction and maintenance of single-skin air-supported structures. British Standards Institution.
BS 5268-4.2	Structural use of timber. Fire resistance of timber structures. Recommendations for calculating fire resistance of timber stud walls and joisted floor constructions. British Standards Institution.

Design principles of fire safety. The Stationery Office, 1996. ISBN 0 11 753045 X.

Chemicals (Hazard Information and Packaging for Supply) Regulations 2002, SI 2002/1689. The Stationery Office, 2002. ISBN 0 11 042419 0. Supporting guides: *The idiot's guide to CHIP 3: Chemicals (Hazard Information and Packaging for Supply) Regulations 2002,* INDG350. HSE Books, 2002. ISBN 0 7176 2333 5 (single copy free or priced packs of 5); *CHIP for everyone,* HSG228. HSE Books, 2002. ISBN 0 7176 2370 X.

Guidance on the acceptance of electronic locks to doors required for means of escape. The Chief Fire Officers' Association.

Ensuring best practice for passive fire protection in buildings. Building Research Establishment, 2003. ISBN 1 870409 19 1.

Smoke shafts protecting fire shafts: their performance and design, BRE Project Report 79204. Building Research Establishment, 2002.

Fire safety of PTFE-based material used in building, BRE Report 274. Building Research Establishment, 1994. ISBN 0 851256 53 8.

Fires and human behaviour. David Fulton Publishers, 2000. ISBN 1 85346 105 9.

Management of health and safety at work. Management of Health and Safety at Work Regulations 1999. Approved code of practice and guidance, L21 (second edition). HSE Books, 2000. ISBN 0 7176 2488 9.

Index

Page numbers in italics refer to information in Figures or Tables.

A

access for firefighters 23, 24, 66–7, 68, 73, 123, 128, 129, 130, 140
aerosols 13, 48, 49–50
alarms *see* fire detection and warning systems
alterations 8, 42, 46, 52–3, 62, 67, 74
alterations notices 6, 8, 9, 36, 38, 43, 53, 142
arson 12, 16, 18, 19, 46, 47, 48, 56–7
assembly points 41, 121, 124
automatic fire detection systems 20, 21, 47, 53, 60, 83, 87, 91, 100, 110, 136–7, 139, 142

B

basements 47, 48, 49, 68, 87, *88,* 102, 111, 142
bedrooms
    automatic fire detection and warning
    systems 60
    bedding 55
    doors 18, 56
    as refuges 30, 74
building work 8, 46, 52–3

C

candles 12
cavity barriers 74, 133
ceilings
    fire-resisting 29, 31, 53, 74, 132
    lining materials 13, 19, 29, 54, 132, 134
children 6, 15, 39, 59, 142, 147
    evacuating 58, 122
CLASP (Consortium of Local Authorities Special Programme) construction method 133
close down procedures 41, 121, 122, 125
co-operation and co-ordination 6, 7, 37, 38, 39, 40, 123
competent persons 4, 6, 10, 129, 130, 143
conduction, fire spreading by 16, 17
construction, fire-resisting 28–9, 30, 55, 57, 72, 73–4, 80, 83, *84–5,* 90, 96, 132–5, 144
contingency plans 121, 122
contractors
    certifying 34, 127, 137
    fire safety training 6, 7, 38, 121, 124
    managing 52–3
    permit to work 52
    risk to 14, 21
    source of ignition 12, 18, 52
convection, fire spreading by 16
cooking 10, 12, 47, 53, 54, 60, 61, 64, 65, 124

D

dangerous substances 7, 13, 14, 40, 46, 122, 143
    storage 19, 48–50
day care centres 4, 50
dead ends
    escape routes 73, 82–7, 143
    fire alarms 83
delayed evacuation 24, 27, 30, 72, 73
dentist surgeries 60
disability *see* people with special needs
Disability Discrimination Act 1995 58
display materials 13, 56
doors
    door-fastenings 18, 29, 33, 34, 60, 88, 98, 116, 128, 129, 138–9, 142
    door furniture 136–8
    final exit 29, 31, 98, 126
    fire-resisting 30, 53, 55, 67, 72, 74, 87, 96, 135–9, 144
    glazing 83, 136
    maintenance 7, 17, 33, 34, 128, 129, 130, 138
    notices 85, 113, 114, 139
    revolving 97
    roller shutter doors 69, 97–8, 129
    self-closing 30, 69, 72, 74, 88, 95, 114, 129, 130, 136–7, 146
    sliding 97
    vision panels 73, 83, *137,* 146
    wicket 97

E

electrical safety 12, 16, 18, 46, 48, 50, 64, 121
emergency escape lighting 32, 100, 111–12, 121, 143
    tests, checks and maintenance 33, 34, 112, 116, 128, 129, 130
    torches 112
emergency plans 30, 31, 36–7, 38–40, 45, 58, 73, 116, 121–2, 123, 124
equipment and machinery 12, 16, 18, 19, 41, 46, 47, 48, 50–1, 64, 121, 125
escape routes 24–5, 145
    age and construction of the premises 28–9, 46, 53, 73
    alternative exits 29, 80, 83, *86,* 87, 88, 90, 91, 93, 99, 104–7, 126, 142
    basements 47, 48, 49, 87, *88,* 102, 111, 142
    corridors 10, 30, 46, 53, 73, 77, 87, 88–9, *92,* 93
    dead ends 73, 82–7, 143

emergency lighting 32, 100, 111–12, 121, 143
escape time 26, 27–8, 31, 75, 78, 100, 124
final exits 24, 29, 31, 64, 72, 73, 78, 87, 97, 98, 99, 126, 143
hatches 98
Hospital Streets 30, 73, 74, 77, 88–9, *100, 104–7, 108–9,* 110, 145
inner rooms 81, *82,* 142, 145, 146
layouts 99–110
levels of risk 29
lifts 30, 41, 76, 96, 100, 129, 143
lobbies 67, 77, 87, 91, *92,* 145
maintenance 7, 30, 31, 33, 34, 73, 95, 96
managing 30, 31, 139
number required 29–30, 73, 77, 99, 110, 138
obstructions 28, *29,* 30, 31, 34, 46, 53, 73, 91, 98, 99, 128
people with special needs 17, 30, 75–7, 89
reception areas 94
roof exits 77, 96, *97*
seating and gangways
signs and notices 32, 33, 111, 113–15, 121, 129
suitability 30, 73–4
tests and checks 35, 73, 128, 129, 130
training 28, 30, 41, 124, 125
travel distance 20, 21, 27–8, 73, 77–9, 81, 82, 91, 99, 100, 101–2, 110, 146
type and number of people using premises 20, 25, 29, 31, 73, 74, 81, 91, 99, 102
widths and capacity of 29–30, 53, 73, 77, 93
see also doors; stairways
evacuation
delayed 24, 27, 30, 72, 73
phased 21, 61, 66, 145
progressive horizontal 21, 27, 30, 41, 70–2, 74, 91, 145
single stage 27, 28, 66, 70
strategy 26–7, 57–8, 70–3, 75, 76
vertical 91, 110
extinguishers 22–3, 24, 33, 34, 63–5, 114, 116, 128, 129

F
false alarms 22, 61, 62, 116, 143
fire
classes of 63–4
spread of 10, 13, 16–17, 31, 46, 53, 54–6, 74, 96, 133
fire blankets 47, 65, 116
fire certificates 5, 55
fire dampers 47, 56, 74
fire detection and warning systems 21–2
alarm receiving station/centre 126, 128, 142
automatic fire detection systems 20, 21, 47, 53, 60, 83, 87, 91, 100, 110, 136–7, 139, 142
auxiliary power supply 22, 62
false alarms 22, 61, 62, 116, 143
manual call points 21, 60, 61, 121, 126, 137

monitoring 22, 34, 42, 57, 59, 61, 126
phased evacuation 21, 61
quality assurance 127
record-keeping 34, 35, 62, 116
smoke detectors 60, 61, 81, 87, 137, 146
sound levels 22, 59
staff alarms 61
staged alarms 61, 146
tests and checks 7, 33, 34, 35, 61–2, 116, 124, 126, 128, 129, 130
voice alarms 21, 58, 59, 129
fire drills 41, 42, 116, 125–6
fire hazard rooms 55–6, 110, 121
fire marshals 23, 42, 125, 126, 141
fire-resisting separation 52, 53, 55, 57, 94, 132–5
fire risk assessment
aims 9
co-operation and co-ordination 6, 7, 37, 38, 39, 40, 123
emergency plans 30, 31, 36–7, 38–40, 45, 58, 73, 116, 121–2, 123, 124, 140
evaluating risk 9, *11,* 16–18, 36, 123
Fire Safety Order and 5–8, 10, 147
flexibility 20
historic buildings 5, 73, 140–1
identifying fire hazards 9, *11,* 12–14, 36, *117–20, 131*
identifying people at risk *11,* 14–15, 36, 98, *117–20,* 123, *131*
information and instruction 6, 7, 32–3, 37, 38–9, 40, 113–15, 121, 122–3, 125, 126
method 9–10
plan of action 45, 57–8
record-keeping 6, 8, 9, *11,* 36–7, 43, 116, *117–20, 131*
removing or reducing fire hazards 9, 18–20, 36, 45, 46, 57, *117–20, 131*
removing or reducing risk to people 5, 20–35, 36, 45, 46, 57, *131*
reviewing 8, *11,* 42–3, 121, *131*
sources of fuel 12, 13, 19, 30, 46, 47–50, 57
sources of ignition 12–13, 16, 18, 30, 48, 49, 51–2, 53, 57
sources of oxygen 12, 14, 19
fire safety audit 116, 121
fire safety management 5, 9, 15, 35, 45, 52–3, 56, 139
fire safety manager 124, 144
Fire Safety Order 5–8, 10, 147
fire safety strategy 23, 66, 116, 144
fire stopping 53, 74, 88, 134, 144
fire suppression systems 42, 49, 65–6, 67, 77, 116, 121, 129
automatic 23, 47, 57, 58, 72, 87, 100, 110, 142
Firecode documents 70, 74, *119*
firefighters' switches 33, 66, 69, 130
firefighting equipment and facilities 22–4

access for firefighters 23, 24, 66–7, 68, 73, 128, 129, 130, 140
  extinguishers 22–3, 24, 33, 34, 63–5, 114, 116, 128, 129
  firefighters' switches 33, 66, 69, 130
  firefighting lifts and shafts 30, 66, 67, 76, 96, 123, 129, 144
  foam inlets 23, 68–9
  hose reels 23, 34, 65, 116
  hydrants 69, 128, 129, 130
  maintenance 7, 23, 24, 33, 34, 65–6, 67, 68, 69, 116, 128, 129, 130
  quality assurance 127
  rising mains 23, 66, 68, 69, 121, 130
  signs 22, 24, 32, 33, 66, 114
  tests and checks 35, 65, 69, 128, 129, 130
  training 23, 39, 41, 63, 65, 124, 125
  see also fire suppression systems
flame-retardant materials 54–5, 134
flammable liquids 13, 19, 48–9, 50, 57, 63, 64, 144
floors
  covering materials 13, 19, 135
  fire-resisting 29, 31, 53, 57, 74, 87, 96, 132–3, 135
foam, fire risk of 13, 55
foam inlets 23, 68–9
fuel, sources of 12, 13, 19, 30, 46, 47–50, 57
furniture and furnishings 13, 42, 53, 54–5

G
gas cylinders 14, 19, 41, 49, 50, 53
  see also aerosols; LPG; medical gases
glass, fire-resisting 83, 136
GP surgeries 10, 32, 60, 101–3

H
hatches 98
hazard
  definition 9
  identifying fire hazards 9, 11, 12–14, 36, 117–20, 131
  removing or reducing 9, 18–20, 36, 45, 46, 57, 131
hazardous materials 19, 41, 42, 123, 140, 144
health centres 85, 101–3
healthcare premises 144
  access for firefighters 67
  automatic fire detection and warning systems 60
  emergency plan 38
  evacuation strategy 26–7, 57–8, 70–3
  fire risk assessment 29
  flame-retardant materials 134
  minimum fire resistance 132
heating 12, 18, 50–1, 53, 54
historic buildings 5, 73, 140–1

hose reels 23, 34, 65, 116
hospitals 4
  access for firefighters 67
  escape routes 30, 74, 104–9
  fire-resisting construction 55
  firefighting equipment and facilities 63
  Hospital Streets 30, 73, 74, 77, 88–9, 100, 104–7, 108–9, 110, 145
  Nucleus fire precautions 45, 46, 59, 69, 70, 100, 108–9, 148
housekeeping 41, 46

I
ignition, sources of 12–13, 16, 18, 30, 48, 49, 51–2, 53, 57
information and instruction 6, 7, 32–3, 37, 38–9, 40, 113–15, 121, 122–3, 125, 126
insulated core panels 46, 53–4

L
ladders 98
laundries 10, 13, 46, 47, 60
lifts
  escape routes 30, 41, 76, 96, 100, 129, 143
  firefighting 30, 66, 67, 76, 96, 123, 129, 144
lighting 12, 16, 58, 69, 112, 115
lightning 46
LPG 13, 49, 51, 53
luminaires 111, 112, 128, 129, 130

M
maintenance
  checklist 128–30
  emergency escape lighting 33, 34, 112, 116, 128, 129, 130
  equipment and machinery 18, 19, 50, 51
  escape routes 7, 30, 31, 33, 34, 73, 95, 96
  fire detection and warning systems 7, 33, 34, 35, 61–2, 116, 124, 128, 129, 130
  fire doors 7, 17, 33, 34, 128, 129, 130, 138
  firefighting equipment and facilities 7, 23, 24, 33, 34, 35, 65–6, 67, 68, 69, 116, 128, 129, 130
medical gases 14, 19, 48, 50
  see also gas cylinders; piping
multi-occupied buildings 4, 6
  co-operation and co-ordination 40, 123
  escape routes 91
  fire detection and warning systems 21
  fire risk assessment 10, 15
  information and instruction 113

N
naked flame 12, 18, 53
Nucleus fire precautions 45, 46, 59, 69, 70, 100, 108–9, 148

O

out-patient clinics 29, 71, *85*
oxygen, sources of 12, 14, 19

P

partitions, fire-resisting 28, 53, 132, 133, 134
   see also walls
patients
   escape routes 70–3, 74–8, 87, 90, 93, 96,
   98–9, 99–100, 101–2, 104–7
   evacuating 25, 26–8, 31, 41, 57, 58, 60, 110,
   121, 124, 126
   fire detection and warning systems 21–2
   fire risk assessment 15, 17, 116, *117–20*
   information and instruction 38, 39, 40, 41,
   121, 125, 126
   source of ignition 13
   staff observation 59, 99, 110
people at risk
   evaluating 16–18, 72
   identifying *11,* 14–15, 36, 98, *117–20,*
   123, *131*
   removing or reducing risk 5, 20–35, 36, 45,
   57, *117–20, 131*
   restricting the spread of fire and smoke 54–6
   type and number using premises 20, 25, 29,
   31, 42, 73, 74, 81, 91, 99, 102
people with special needs
   evacuating 17, 30–1, 41, 46, 57–8, 75–7, 89,
   121, 124, 125, 126
   fire risk assessment 6, 10, *11,* 15, 17, 57–8
   fire warning systems 59, 60
   information and instruction 39, 112, 113,
   123, 125, 126
   risk to 15, 42
personal emergency evacuation plans (PEEPs)
58, 125
phased evacuation 21, 61, 66, 145
physiotherapy departments 12
piping 14, 19, 50, 53, 55
plans and specifications 36, 37, 67, 121
portable appliance testing (PAT) 51
progressive horizontal evacuation 21, 27, 30,
41, 70–2, 74, 91, 145
protected areas 24, 29, 31, *71,* 72, 74, 75,
77, 145
   see also refuge areas

R

radiation, fire spreading by 16, 17
reception areas 94
record-keeping
   emergency escape lighting 112, 116
   fire detection and warning systems 34, 35,
   62, 116
   fire risk assessment 6, 8, 9, *11,* 36–7, 43,
   116, *117–20, 131*
   fire safety training 42, 125

refuge areas 30, 70–1, 72, 75, *76,* 100, 110,
121, 145
   see also protected areas
residential care premises 4
rising mains 23, 66, 68, 69, 121, 130
risk
   definition 9
   evaluating 9, *11,* 16–18, 36, 123
   people at risk *11,* 14–15, 36, 98, *117–20,*
   123, *131*
   reducing 5, *11,* 36, 45, 46, 57
roll calls 123, 126
roller shutter doors 69, 97–8, 129
roofs
   fire risk assessment 57
   roof exits 77, 96, *97*

S

SCOLA (Second Consortium of Local
Authorities) construction method 133
security 29, 33, 57, 98–9, 138, 139
shafts, firefighting *see* lifts
signs and notices 22, 24, 32–3, 69, 111,
113–15, 129
   information and instruction 39, 66, 85, 97,
   121, 139
single stage evacuation 27, 28, 66, 70
smoke
   control of 29, 31, 47, 56, 60, 66, 68, 87, 88,
   116, 130, 135
   dangers of 17, 54
   smoke dampers 47, 56
   spread of 16–18, 33, 46, 53, 54, 74, 96
Smoke and Heat Exhaust Ventilation Systems
(SHEVS) 56, 60, 68, 116, 130
smoke detectors 60, 61, 81, 87, 137, 146
smoking 12, 16, 18, 46, 48, 50, 51–2, 124
sprinklers 23, 42, 47, 49, 65–6, 67, 110,
121, 125, 129
staff
   evacuating patients 26–8
   fire drills 41, 42, 116, 125–6
   fire safety training 7, 20, 22, 23, 28, 30, 36,
   39, 40–2, 63, 65, 72, 124–6, 139
   information and instruction 7, 32–3, 38–9,
   40, 114–15, 121, 122–3
   patient observation 59, 99, 110
   staff alarms 61
   staff numbers 45, 71, 72, 73, 74–5, 77,
   110, 138
   see also contractors
stairways
   accommodation stairways 94–5, 142
   basements 87, 102
   bypass routes 93, *94*
   external 95, 143
   hazards in 10, 30, 46, 53, 91
   protected 24, 28, 87, 89–93, 95, 96, 99

spiral and helical 96
width and capacity of 77, 89
storage 19, 42, 46, 47–50, 53, 57

T

telephones 33, 66, 123
torches 112
training
    fire safety 6, 7, 20, 22, 28, 30, 36, 38–9,
    40–2, 72, 121, 124–6, 139
    firefighting equipment 23, 39, 41, 63, 65,
    124, 125
    record-keeping 42, 125
treatment centres 10, 74

V

vandalism 19, 65
vehicles 50
ventilation systems 14, 17, 19, 42, 47, 50,
56, 130
vertical evacuation 91, 110
vision panels 73, 81, 83, *137,* 146
voids 48, 53, 55, 74, 133, 140

W

walls
    fire-resisting 29, 30, 31, 53, 57, 67, 74,
    95, 132
    insulated core panels 46, 53–4
    lining materials 13, 19, 29, 54, 132, 134
    see also partitions
waste and packaging, combustible 13, 16, 19,
46, 52, 57
way guidance systems 32, 112, 146
windows, fire-resisting 83, 95, 96
    vision panels 73, 81, 83, *137,* 146

X

X-ray departments 12